Construction (Design and Management) Regulations 2007

Guidance for Principal Contractors

CONTENTS

1. INTRODUCTION   **4**

  A. How to use this publication   4

  B. Who is this guidance for?   4

  C. Introduction to CDM 2007 Regulations   4

  D. Main changes to the 2007 CDM Regulations   5

2. SUMMARY OF CDM DUTYHOLDERS   **7**

  A. Clients   7

  B. CDM Co-ordinator   8

  C. Designer   10

  D. Contractors and the self-employed   14

  E. Workers   15

3. THE PRINCIPAL CONTRACTOR   **17**

  A. Introduction   17

  B. Duties   18

    a) Client Involvement   19

    b) Principal Contractor Competence   19

    c) Planning/Managing   20

    d) Contractors (including client appointed)   20

    e) Information to Contractors   21

    f) Co-operation and Co-ordination   22

    g) Health and Safety Plan   22

    h) Competence of those appointed by Principal Contractor   23

    i) Welfare Facilities   23

    j) Control of Access   24

    k) Site Rules   25

    l) Passing on Information   25

    m) Design Changes   25

    n) Health and Safety File   26

    o) Induction and Training   27

    p) Workforce Involvement   27

    q) Legal Notice   28

4. WHO DOES WHAT, WHEN (poster included)

5. ANNEXES

5. ANNEXES   29
  A. The Management of Health and Safety   29
  B. The Principles of Prevention   34
  C. Competences   39
  D. Pre-Construction Information   46
  E. The Construction Phase Plan   49
  F. The Health and Safety File   52
  G. Contracts   55
  H. Inductions   58
  I. Worker Involvement/Consultation   60
  J. FAQ's   64
  K. Differences between CDM 1994 and CDM 2007   89
  L. Differences between CHSW 1996 and CDM 2007   91
  M. CDM 2007 – CHSW Requirements   101
  N. References   106

1. INTRODUCTION

A. How to use this publication

This publication is intended to give guidance to principal contractors on how to comply with the Construction (Design and Management) Regulations 2007 (CDM 2007).

It should be read in conjunction with CDM 2007 Regulations and ACoP published by HSC.

The guide is set out to inform who can fulfil the role of principal contractor, what they must do, what they must expect from other dutyholders and clarifies what principal contractors are not expected to do. The Annex's provide additional information to the main text, as well as Annex J – FAQ's, and Annex N – References.

B. Who is the guidance for?

This publication is mainly aimed at organisations who fulfil the role of principal contractor under CDM 2007.

It also serves to inform main and managing contractors of good practice, even if their work does not fall within CDM notifiable projects scope and no formal appointments need to be made.

Other CDM dutyholders may also find this publication useful to clarify what they may expect from principal contractors. The Regulations encourage cooperation between all of the dutyholders and it is important to understand the roles of all of the other parties.

C. INTRODUCTION TO CDM 07

i. Aim

These Regulations concern occupational health, safety and welfare in construction. They place duties in relation to management arrangements and practical measures on a range of construction project participants, including clients, designers and contractors.

These Regulations are intended to focus attention on planning and management throughout construction projects, from design concept onwards. The concept is for health and safety considerations to be treated as an essential, but normal part of a project's development – not an afterthought or bolt-on extra.

The key aim of CDM2007 is to integrate health and safety into the management of the project and to encourage everyone involved to work together

ii. Approach

The effort devoted to planning and managing health and safety should be in proportion to the risks and complexity associated with the project. When deciding what you need to do to comply with these Regulations, your focus should always be on action necessary to reduce and manage risks. Any paperwork produced should help with communication and risk management. Paperwork that adds little to the management of risk is a waste of effort, and can be a dangerous distraction from the real business of risk reduction and management.

i Key Benefits
The key benefits of this approach are
- improve the planning and management of projects from the very start;
- identify hazards early on, so they can be eliminated or reduced at the design or planning stage and the remaining risks can be properly managed;
- target effort where it can do the most good in terms of health and safety; and
- discourage unnecessary bureaucracy.
- time and thought invested at the start of the project will pay dividends not only in improved health and safety, but also in:
  - reductions in the overall cost of ownership, because the structure is designed for safe and easy maintenance and cleaning work, and because key information is available in the health and safety file;
  - reduced delays;
  - more reliable costings and completion dates;
  - improved communication and co-operation between key parties; and
  - improved quality of the finished product.

D. MAIN CHANGES TO THE CDM 2007 REGULATIONS
Issues Principal Contractors need to be aware of:

The main changes to CDM 2007 when compared with CDM 1994 (as modified in 2000) relate mainly to client, CDM co-ordinator and designer duties.

In summary, the duties of the principal contractors and contractors do not change in any significant way apart from what they can expect from other dutyholders. There is considerable emphasis within the Regulations on cooperation between all of the parties. In particular there are very clear requirements to involve the workforce.

Whilst the co-operation requirements already exist in CDM in the interest of promoting good health and safety practices, good co-operation should assist a smooth running project with no surprises emerging.

The other main change in CDM 2007 from CDM 1994 is in its layout and content. The Construction (Health, Safety and Welfare) Regulations 1996 were introduced as a set of Regulations specific to work on construction sites. Since

1996, other Regulations have come into being which have superseded these construction-specific Regulations and which apply to all industries. The Work at Height Regulations 2005 is an example where new Regulations have come into being and the sections relating to work at height (falls) within the Construction (Health, Safety and Welfare) Regulations 1996 have been revoked, and the regulations as a whole incorporated into CDM 2007. For more information on the differences between CHSW 1996 and CDM 2007 see Annex L.

The CDM Regulations 2007 therefore forms a single set of Construction legislation. It is set out as:-

Part 1 – Introduction

Part 2 – General Management Duties Applying to Construction Projects

Part 3 – Additional Duties where Project is Notifiable

Part 4 – Duties Relating to Health and Safety on Construction Sites

Part 5 – General

Note that Part 3 only applies to projects that are notifiable under Regulation 2(3) that states,

"For the purpose of these Regulations, a Project is notifiable if the construction phase is likely to involve more than –

- *30 days, or*
- *500 person days of construction work."*

For more information on the differences between CDM 1994 and CDM 2007 see Annex K.

2. SUMMARY OF CDM DUTYHOLDERS

A. CLIENTS

The role of the client has been given a higher profile in CDM 2007 to provide leadership to the construction team and to be made clearly accountable for the impact their approach has on health and safety of those working on or affected by the project.

However, it is recognised that clients may not have the expertise or resources to plan and manage projects themselves but they are required to ensure that arrangements are in place to ensure that duties of others under CDM 2007 are carried out. There is also a duty to see that the arrangements, once agreed, are working.

Clients are also expected to take an active role in co-operating with the CDM co-ordinator in creating the pre-construction information. In particular, the client should consider any specific requirements they have at this point in the procurement process so as to avoid change and possible conflict at a later point in time. Issues such as access points and any rules for contracting organisations in occupied premises need to be considered.

It should be noted that in some forms of procurement, the role of the client may shift to different parties (e.g. in PFI/PPP forms of contract). Clients should anticipate this and make suitable arrangements.

Where a project is notifiable under CDM 2007, clients must appoint a CDM co-ordinator and a principal contractor. It is good practice for clients to consider for all projects (notifiable or not) if they need health and safety assistance to ensure compliance with other legislation such as the Management of Health and Safety at Work Regulations 1999.

i. What clients must do-

For all projects:

Regulations 4-10

Clients must make sure that:

- Designers, contractors and other team members that they propose to engage are competent (or work under the supervision of a competent person), adequately resourced and appointed as early as is practicable;
- They allow sufficient time for each stage of the project, from concept onwards;
- They co-operate with others involved with the project as is necessary to allow them to comply with their duties under the regulations;
- They co-ordinate their own work with others involved with the project in order to ensure that safety of those carrying out the construction work, and others who may be affected by it;

- There are effective management arrangements in place throughout the life of the project to ensure that the construction work can be carried out safely and without risk to health (This does not mean managing the work themselves, as few clients have the expertise and resources needed and it can cause confusion);
- All parties are clear on their role and how it interfaces with other parties;
- Suitable welfare facilities are provided by the principal contractor for those carrying out the construction work;
- Any fixed workplace (e.g. offices, shops, factories, schools) that is being built will comply with any requirements of the Workplace (Health and Safety) Regulations 1992; and
- Relevant information likely to be needed by designers, contractors or others to plan and manage their work is passed to them in order to comply with Regulation 10;
- They give sufficient notice to contractors of the minimum time contractors will be given for planning and preparation between appointment and starting work;

ii. For notifiable projects
Regulations 14,15,16 and 17

For notifiable projects, in addition to the duties set out above, clients have to:
- Appoint a CDM co-ordinator to advise them and assist with their duties – mainly in the design and planning stages but to include any design changes during the construction phase;
- Appoint a principal contractor to plan and manage the construction work – if possible this should be early enough for them to advise on buildability and maintainability;
- Ensure that the construction phase of notifiable projects does not start until the principal contractor has prepared a suitably developed health and safety plan and made arrangements for suitable and sufficient welfare facilities to be present from the start of the work; (See Annexe M)
- Ensure the health and safety file is prepared, reviewed, or updated ready for handover at the end of the construction work. The completed file must then be kept available for any future construction work or to pass on to a new owner.

B. CDM CO-ORDINATOR
A new role of CDM co-ordinator has been created by the CDM Regulations 2007. The CDM co-ordinator's role may be summed up as being 'The client's adviser in matters relating to construction health and safety'. The role is wider than the

previous role of the planning supervisor and involves advising and assisting the client in undertaking the measures he needs to take to comply with CDM 2007, including in particular the clients duties in relation to the start of the construction phase and during the construction phase.

i. What CDM Co-ordinators must do-

For all projects:

Regulations 4 to 7,20 and 21

The CDM co-ordinator's duties include ensuring that suitable arrangements are made **and are implemented** for the co-ordination of health and safety measures during planning and preparation for the construction phase.

They are responsible for co-ordinating: -

- the contents of the Health and Safety File;
- the information the principal contractor needs to prepare the construction phase plan;
- any design development that may affect planning and management of the construction phase. This will in particular include management of changes to design during the construction phase where co-operation is needed between designers, principal contractors and contractors. CDM coordinators must recognise that during the construction phase the site is controlled by the principal contractor who remains responsible for implementing good practice. A good way of carrying out this duty could be to have sight of the construction phase plan as it develops.

In summary, CDM co-ordinators should advise and assist clients with their duties, in particular:

Appointing competent designers and contractors; and

- Ensure that adequate arrangements are in place for managing the project;
- Notifying HSE about the project;
- Co-ordinating design work, planning and other preparation for construction where relevant to health and safety;
- Locating the information needed by designers and contractors (the pre-construction information) and advising the client if surveys need to be commissioned to fill significant gaps;
- Managing the flow of health and safety information between clients, designers and contractors;
- Advising the client on the suitability of the initial construction phase plan and the arrangements made to ensure that welfare facilities are on site from the start of the project;
- Producing or updating a relevant, user friendly, Health and Safety File

suitable for future use at the end of the construction phase.

It is essential to fully understand the role of the CDM co-ordinator and hence understand what they do **not** have to do. **They do not have to**:

- Approve the appointment of designers, principal contractors or contractors, although they normally advise clients about competence and resources;

- Approve or check designs, although they have to be satisfied that the design process addresses the need to eliminate and controls risks;

- Approve the principal contractor's construction phase plan, although they have to be able to advise clients on its adequacy at the start of construction;

- Supervise the principal contractor's implementation of the construction phase plan; or

- Supervise or monitor construction work – this is the responsibility of the principal contractor.

- Deal directly with parties under the control of the principal contractor who does have a duty to co-operate in order to let the CDM co-ordinator carry out his tasks.

C. DESIGNER

CDM 2007 recognises the key role designers have in construction health and safety projects.

Designers shall not commence work in relation to the project unless their client is aware of their duties under the Regulations. This, in turn, will help ensure that the client's requirements are clearly understood by encouraging discussion and co-operation.

A new duty placed on the designer is so far as is reasonably practicable to 'eliminate hazards which may give rise to risks' and to 'reduce risks from any remaining hazards'. This is a new requirement and requires designers to consider if they are introducing a hazardous material or process. In practice there are potential hazards in almost everything so that a pragmatic view will need to be taken on all of the factors to be considered in the design. These factors will include health and safety, cost, fitness for purpose, aesthetics, buildability, maintenance and environmental impact. The Regulations do not prescribed design outcomes but they do require designers to weigh the various factors and to reach reasoned, professional decisions.

Put simply, designers must not produce designs that cannot be constructed, used and maintained in reasonable safety and with proper consideration of health issues.

Designers need to recognise the amount of effort put in to eliminating hazards and reducing risk should depend upon the degree of risk.

i. Who are designers?

Designers include **everyone** who prepare or specify designs for construction work, including variations. This is not just the drawings, design details and specifications but specifiers of quality and including lists of specific requirements and even materials which they wish to prohibit.

A client may become a designer by insisting upon a specific material or design detail they may wish to see incorporated. A contractor may become a designer by designing specific details of their section of work or by temporary works required for the project.

Designers therefore include:

- Architects, civil and structural engineers, building surveyors, landscape architects, other consultants, manufacturers and design practices (of whatever discipline) contributing to, or having overall responsibility for, any part of the design, for example drainage engineers designing the drainage for a new development;

- Anyone who specifies or alters a design, or who specifies the use of a particular method of work or material, such as a design manager, quantity surveyor who insists on specific material or a client who stipulates a particular layout for a new building;

- Building service designers, engineering practices or others designing plant which forms part of the permanent structure (including lifts, heating, ventilation and electrical systems), for example a specialist provider of permanent fire extinguisher installations;

- Those purchasing materials where the choice has been left open, for example those purchasing building blocks and so deciding the weights that bricklayers must handle;

- Contractors carrying out design work as part of their contribution to a project, such as an engineering contractor providing design, procurement and construction management services;

- Temporary works engineers, including those designing auxiliary structures, such as formwork, falsework, façade retention schemes, scaffolding, and sheet piling;

- Interior designers, including shop-fitters who also develop the design;

- Heritage organisations who specify how work is to be done in detail, for example providing detailed requirements to stabilise existing structures and;

- Those determining how building and structures are altered, e.g. during refurbishment where this has the potential for partial or complete collapse.

Local authority or government officials may provide advice relating to designs and relevant statutory requirements, e.g. the building regulations, but this does not make them designers. This is because these are 'fixed' requirements where the designer has no choice in respect of compliance. However, if the statutory bodies require that particular features which are not statutory requirements and included or excluded (e.g. stipulating) the use of Hazardous substances for cleaning or the absence of edge protection on flat roofs), then they are designers and must ensure that they comply with these Regulations.

Designers also need to take account of other relevant health and safety requirements when carrying out design work. Where the structure will be used as a workplace, (for example factories, offices, schools, hospitals) they need to take account of the provisions of the Workplace (Health, Safety and Welfare) Regulations 1992 which relate to the design of, or materials used in the structure. This means taking account of risks directly related to the proposed use of the structure, including associated private roadways and pedestrian routes, and risks arising from the need to clean and maintain the permanent fixtures and fittings. For example, hospitals will need to be designed in a way that will accommodate the safe lifting and movement of patients; food preparation and serving areas will need non-slip floors.

Manufacturers supplying standardised products that can be used in any project are not designers under CDM 2007, although they may have duties under supply legislation. The person who selects the product is a designer and must take account of health and safety issues arising from its use. If a product is purpose-made for a project, the person who prepares the specification is a designer under CDM 2007, and so is the manufacturer who develops the detailed design.

ii. What a designer must do-

Regulations 4, 5, 6, 11, 12 and 18

Designers must:

- Ensure that they are competent to address the health and safety issues likely to arise from the design;
- Ensure that clients are aware of their duties;
- Ensure that, for **notifiable projects**, the client has appointed a CDM co-ordinator and notified HSE (and designers must not start design work unless they have);
- When carrying out design work, eliminate hazards where this is reasonably possible, and reduce risk associated with those hazards which remain, taking account of the information supplied by the client;
- Provide adequate information about any significant risks associated with the design;
- Co-ordinate their work with that of others in order to improve the way in which risks are managed and controlled;
- Co-operate with the CDM co-ordinator, principal contractor and with any

other designers or contractors as necessary to allow them to comply with their duties. This includes providing any information needed for the preconstruction information or health and safety file;

In carrying out these duties, designers need to consider the hazards and risks to those who will:

- Carry out construction work;
- Clean or maintain the permanent fixtures and fittings;
- Use a structure designed as a place of work;
- Demolish all or part of the structure; or
- Who may be affected by such work, for example customers or the general public.

iii. What designers do not have to do-

Under CDM 2007, designers do not have to:

- Take into account or provide information about unforeseeable hazards and risks;
- Consider hazards outside of the workplace
- Design for possible future uses of structures that cannot reasonably be anticipated from their design brief;
- Specify construction methods, except where the design assumes or requires a particular construction or erection sequence, or where a competent contractor might need such information;
- Exercise any health and safety management function over contractors or others; or
- Be concerned about trivial risks.

Designers are not legally required to keep records of the process through which they achieve a safe design, but it can be useful to record why certain key decisions were made. Brief records of the points considered, the conclusions reached, and the basis for those conclusions, can be very helpful when designs are passed from one designer to another. This will reduce the likelihood of important decisions being altered by those who may not fully understand the implications of doing so.

Too much paperwork is a bad as too little, because the useless hides the necessary. Large volumes of paperwork listing generic hazards and risks, most of which are well known to competent contractors and others who use the design are positively harmful, and suggest a lack of understanding on the part of the designer.

D. CONTRACTORS AND THE SELF EMPLOYED

Contractors and their employees, those actually doing the construction work are most at risk of injury and ill-health. They have a key role to play, in cooperation with other duty holders in co-ordination by planning and managing the work to ensure that risks are identified and are properly controlled.

Contractors may include utilities, specialist contractors, contractors nominated by the client and the self-employed. Contractors are often sub-contractors to the principal contractor. Contractors may also have duties as designers if they are involved in designing elements of their work such as pre-cast concrete planks or curtain walling.

Anyone who directly employees, engages construction workers or who manages construction work is a contractor for the purposes of these Regulations. This includes companies that use their own workforce to do construction work on their own premises.

i.   What contractors must do-

Regulations 4-7, 13 and 19

ii.   For all projects all contractors must:

- plan, manage and monitor their own work to make sure that their workers are safe from the start of their work on site;

- satisfy themselves that they and anyone they employ or engage are competent and adequately resourced;

- check clients are aware of their duties. This does not mean that every contractor has to contact the client with duplication of duty but to ensure that the CDM coordinator has made the client aware;

- provide their workers (whether employed or selfemployed) with any necessary information, including about relevant aspects of other contractors' work, and site induction (where not provided by a principal contractor) which they need to work safely, to report problems or to respond appropriately in an emergency;

- ensure that any design work they do complies with Regulation 11 which sets out the duty of designers;

- comply with any requirements listed in Schedule 2 & 3 of the Regulations that apply to their work (Welfare and Inspections);

- co-operate with others and co-ordinate their work with others working on the project. In particular, contractors must have systems in place in order to consult their workforce on health and safety issues.

- obtain specialist advice (e.g. from a structural engineer or occupational hygienist) where necessary when planning high risk-work – e.g. alterations that could result in structural collapse or construction on contaminated land.

iii. In the case of notifiable projects contractors must also:

- check that a CDM co-ordinator has been appointed and HSE notified before they start work. This should be done at a start-up meeting where all duties, responsibilities and management systems are agreed.
- co-operate with the principal contractor, CDM coordinator and others working on the project;
- tell the principal contractor about risks to others created by their work;
- comply with any reasonable directions from the principal contractor, and with any relevant rules in the health and safety plan;
- inform the principal contractor of any problems with the plan or risks identified during their work that have significant implications for the management of the project;
- tell the principal contractor about accidents and dangerous occurrences;
- provide information for the health and safety file;

Where contractors are involved in design work, including for temporary works, they also have duties as designers.

See Annex H for details of what should be in an induction and Annex I for ideas on engaging the workforce to contribute to health and safety.

Note that employers' of workers who suffer death, reportable injury, disease or dangerous occurrence are deemed to be the 'responsible person' and have the responsibility of providing a report to the relevant enforcing authority. For self-employed workers, the 'responsible person' is the contractor they are working for or the principal contractor if working directly for him. In any case, contractors must ensure that they provide information about RIDDOR (Reportable Injuries, Diseases and Dangerous Occurrences Regulations 1995) to the principal contractor so that they can fulfil their own duties.

Details of RIDDOR 1995 and downloadable reporting forms, F2508 and F2508A can be found on the HSE website.

E. WORKERS

Workers, along with all others involved in the life of a Project have duties to co-operate and to co-ordinate with others (The term 'worker' includes managers and supervisors.) They need to be involved at the earliest practicable point in time and should;

    i. Give feedback to their employer via the agreed consultation method

    ii. Give input into risk assessments and developing a method statement from it

    iii. Work to the agreed method statement or approach their employer to discuss implementing any change or improvement

iv. Use welfare facilities with respect

v. Keep tools and PPE in good condition

vi. Be vigilant for hazards and risks and inform management and supervision

vii. Be aware of arrangements and actions to take if a dangerous situation arises

viii. Co-operate with all other parties

3. THE PRINCIPAL CONTRACTOR

A. INTRODUCTION

The principal contractor is the key dutyholder for the construction phase who is required to ensure effective management of health and safety through the construction phase of the project.

Their main duty is to properly plan, manage and co-ordinate work during the construction phase in order to ensure that hazards are identified and risks are properly controlled.

The principal contractor has a duty to liaise with all of the other CDM dutyholders. In particular:

  i.   consulting with the workforce – directly or via their (sub) contractors

  ii. co-operating with designers and CDM co-ordinators - particularly if any changes occur to design;

  iii. ensuring the client is aware of his duties.

However, whilst the principal contractor is under a duty to co-operate and have systems which allow and facilitate co-operation, the duty and responsibility for managing health and safety in the construction phase lies clearly with him.

Principal contractors must be competent to carry out the work they are engaged to do in a safe manner and ensuring proper consideration of the potential effect of their activities on everyone who may be affected by them.

Principal contractors are required to demonstrate to the client that they have sufficient resources including properly trained and experienced staff, to carry out the project.

It is essential that principal contractors are fully aware of the duties of other CDM dutyholders so that they know the level of information they may reasonably expect. Principal contractors must recognise that time is a resource and that they must be allowed to have reasonable time to plan activities with proper regard to health and safety.

Good principal contractors will place health and safety at the front of their agendas and will review the health and safety implications of all decisions. This is of particular importance if changes arise during the project.

Should changes occur, the principal contractor must allow the CDM coordinator to carry out his duties but must at all times retain responsibility for managing his activities and those of his contractors and sub-contractors. The principal contractor MUST be in control of the site for clear commercial responsibility as well as for health and safety reasons.

B. Duties

What principal contractors must do-

Regulations 4 to 7,22, 24-44

Principal contractors must (letter references are from the ACoP):

a) Satisfy themselves that clients are aware of their duties, that for notifiable Projects a CDM co-ordinator has been appointed and HSE notified before they start work;

b) Ensure that they are competent to address the health and safety issues likely to be involved in the management of the construction phase;

c) Ensure that the construction phase is properly planned, managed and monitored, with adequately resourced, competent site management appropriate to the risk and activity;

d) Ensure that every contractor who will work on the project is informed of the minimum amount of time which they will be allowed for planning and preparation before they begin work on site;

e) Ensure that all contractors are provided with the information about the project that they need to enable them to carry out their work safely and without risks to health. Requests from contractors for information should be met promptly;

f) Ensure safe working and co-ordination and co-operation between contractors;

g) Ensure that a suitably developed construction phase plan ('the plan') is:

   • prepared before construction work begins;

   • developed in discussion with, and communicated to, contractors affected by it;

   • implemented;

   • kept up to date as the project progresses and reviewed prior to any significant changes

h) Satisfy themselves that the designers and contractors that they engage are competent and adequately resourced (see Annex C)

i) Ensure suitable welfare facilities are provided from the start of the construction phase, including sanitary conveniences, washing facilities, drinking water, changing rooms and secure storage, facilities for rest including suitable arrangements to ensure meals can be prepared and eaten and a means of boiling water;

j) Take reasonable steps to prevent unauthorised access to the site;

k) Prepare and enforce any necessary site rules;

l) Provide (copies of or access to) relevant parts of the plan and other information to contractors, including the self-employed, in sufficient time for them to plan their work;

m) liaise with the CDM co-ordinator on design carried out during the construction phase, including design by specialist contractors, and any implications this may have on the plan. Communication with parties under the control of the principal contractor must be directed via the principal contractor.

n) Promptly provide the CDM co-ordinator with any information relevant to the health and safety file (See Annexe F);

o) Ensure that all the workers have been provided with suitable health and safety induction; information and training;

p) Ensure that the workforce is effectively consulted about health and safety matters;

q) Display the completed project notification.

To clarify and expand these duties in the order above:

a) CLIENT INVOLVEMENT

The designer and CDM co-ordinators also have a duty to satisfy themselves that clients are aware of their duties;

The principal contractor needs to be aware of the client's duties. In particular to be aware of the duty the client has to take reasonable steps to ensure that the arrangements made (by principal contractors and by others) are suitable to ensure that the construction work can be carried out so far as is reasonably practicable without risk to the health and safety of any person. This does NOT mean that the client has any responsibility to manage health and safety in the construction phase – that rests with the principal contractor.

The client does have a responsibility to ensure that arrangements are in place - and therefore the principal contractor needs the client and the other CDM dutyholders to agree management arrangements and the level of information the client requires to fulfil their duties. This must be done prior to commencing work. It does not require the client to manage these arrangements but to be able to be satisfied that arrangements are in place and are working.

b) PRINCIPAL CONTRACTOR COMPETENCE

Principal contractors must be confident that they are competent, both as a company and as individuals involved in the project.

Whilst it is preferable to have some form of third party assessment, the least that the principal contractor should do will be to use the criteria for a selfassessment.

Clients need to satisfy themselves that principal contractors are competent for the work they will be carrying out so it is good practice for principal contractors to retain the evidence in writing to avoid duplicating work in the future when bidding or carrying out work which is similar in nature.

Principal contractors will likewise need to satisfy themselves on the competency of any party they engage to carry out work for them including contractors and anyone carrying our design on their behalf.

It is essential that principal contractors fully understand the form of contract being used for the project and that the contractual arrangements are such that all parties can efficiently carry out their duties under CDM. A review should take place prior to starting work, and prior to contractors for all key operations starting their work, in order to ensure that everyone fully understands how to carry out their duty as part of a fully co-operating team.

Further Guidance on competences is given in Annex C of this document.

c) PLANNING / MANAGING

Principal contractors need to ensure that the construction phase is properly planned, managed and monitored. They also need to ensure that they have the right quantity and quality of competent management and supervision available.

Planning should commence as early as possible and be an ongoing process through the duration of the project. Principal contractors should involve everyone they need to ensure that work is carried out efficiently and with full consideration of health and safety issues. In particular, the workforce carrying out the tasks must be actively involved in planning their operation. Consultation on methods should be a clear two way process giving an opportunity for both parties to make contributions to decision making.

Consultation can be formal, recorded processes - or for simple issues an interactive toolbox talk or two-way discussion. More information on planning and managing a project can be found in Annex A – The Management of Health and Safety.

d) Contractors (including Client appointed)

It is important that contractors who will be working on the project (often as sub-contractors to the principal contractor) are involved in planning how they will carry out their work safely and with due regard to health as early as is practicable.

They need to consider not only their own direct activities, but also how their activities can affect other trades working around them. As an example, a welder may have his task well controlled with proper PPE and fire hazard control. However, if another trade is working adjacent to him then the welder's fumes may affect them and controls put into place to rectify the situation.

The principal contractor must recognise that time is a resource and must inform contractors of the amount of time they will be allowed for planning and preparation before they begin work on site.

Having a properly managed period before starting on site will also ensure that all parties are fully aware of what they should be doing and thereby assist in the smooth running of the project. It also allows the contractor to use his specialist expertise and can lead to innovative ideas which often lead to cost or time saving solutions.

Client appointed Contractor (nominated)

On some projects contractors may be appointed directly by the client, often as nominated sub-contractors to the principal contractor. In these cases, the principal contractor must still satisfy themselves that the nominated subcontractor has the correct competences and resource to carry out their scope of works safely and with due regard to health. Should the principal contractor have concerns over such competence and resources, they should liaise with the nominated sub-contractor on how to provide such competence and resource. If satisfactory arrangements cannot be made, the Principal Contractor should refuse the nomination.

The client may also appoint contractors to work directly for them as 'Employer's Persons'. In these cases, the principal contractor must recognise the need to co-ordinate their activities within the overall project. The principal contractor will also have the right to set down reasonable rules that the appointed contractors should meet. It is advisable to discuss with the client prior to appointment of the contractor how the client will manage his performance and ensure that the principal contractor can carry out all of their duties.

e) INFORMATION TO CONTRACTORS

It is the duty of principal contractors to provide contractors with all of the available relevant information they need to enable them to carry out their work safely and without risk to health.

Information should be provided as early as possible and updated if additional information becomes available.

Contractors should either be given copies of the pre tender information (or the relevant parts) or be given access to any relevant information.

Principal contractors should add any other available information such as plans for shared welfare facilities or shared construction items such as use of scaffold. They should also provide copies of the programme so as to clearly show time allotted for activities and other adjacent activities where coordination is required.

Health and safety matters should be clearly addressed at any pre-contract meeting so that all parties are clear in relation to their duties. A further prestart meeting should take place prior to starting work to update plans and to ensure that contractors have carried out their duties such as;

    i.   Risk assessments and method statements

ii. Communicating with the workforce, including familiarisation with their method statement

iii. Providing competent management and supervisors

iv. Providing competent workers

For more information on contracts and CDM 2007, see Annex G.

f) CO-OPERATION AND CO-ORDINATION

The principal contractor has a duty to ensure safe working and co-ordination and co-operations between contractors.

This is an essential process to ensure that all contractors on the project are aware on an ongoing basis of what is expected of them, when it will be done and how. It also serves to clarify what risks may arise from the activities of others working nearby. Where there are shared facilities (e.g. use of scaffold) then this can be agreed so no unexpected risks are created.

Planning co-ordination and co-operation is usually addressed by holding regular co-ordination meetings through the project and at any key activity, such as a new phase or activity commencing.

Major decisions should be recorded via minutes or a file note and made available to everyone who needs to know of such decisions.

Consideration should be given on those invited to attend. As an example, whilst it is essential that the CDM co-ordinator is present at meetings relating to design, it may be good practice to involve them in other meetings or let them have relevant minutes so they can keep up with the project and fulfil their duties. It must be clearly understood that the principal contractor must manage the project and the CDM co-ordinator must only deal with parties contracted to the principal contractor via him. It is not necessary for all parties to attend every meeting and attendance should be selective.

Principal contractors need to recognise that from time to time they may need help from a party or parties outside of the regular project team if there is a need for specific expertise.

g) CONSTRUCTION PHASE PLAN

The principal contractor must ensure that a construction phase plan is developed to a suitable stage by their team before construction work begins.

The plan must be workable, real and regularly reviewed. The plan must be sufficiently developed to allow work to commence and properly address early issues such as mobilisation, welfare, demolition and ground works. It is, however, recognised that some trades later in the construction process may not have their contractors identified and the construction phase plan must be expanded using their specific knowledge prior to commencing that activity.

Input from the client, designers and CDM co-ordinator needs to be taken into account. It is the duty of the client's team to provide pre-construction information identifying hazards and risks of which they are aware after taking all reasonable steps (e.g. contaminated ground, asbestos, services etc.). This pre-construction information also gives the client's team an opportunity to set out any specific rules they may have (e.g. parking rules or access to occupied premises). Principal contractors should ensure that information they may reasonably require is clearly identified and allowance made for any requirements within the tender sum. The information should be taken into account when compiling the construction phase Plan.

The construction phase plan is not a document to compile at the start of the project and then simply be filed away. It should be considered a live document, reviewed as new activities commence, changes are incorporated or programme changes alter the interfacing of activities.

Many principal contractors create their plan within a framework of integrated management incorporating health, safety, environment and quality management. The plan will therefore consist of plans for each activity, taking proper account of how best to manage health and safety with due regard to the environment and to the quality defined by the client. This approach provides one definitive plan rather than separate plans which may duplicate or even contradict each other.

The plan should include an audit process to confirm that it is working properly and to provide feedback for future projects.

See Annex D for more details on Pre-Construction information, and Annex E for more information on the Construction Phase Plan.

h) COMPETENCE OF THOSE APPOINTED BY THE PRINCIPAL CONTRACTOR

As noted above, principal contractors must ensure that anyone they engage are competent and adequately resourced.

Annex C gives a framework on how to assess competence. The degree of work involved should reflect the level of risk in activities and not be an over bureaucratic process.

i) WELFARE FACILITIES

CDM requires that the principal contractor provide suitable welfare facilities from the start of the project.

Details of what is required are available on HSE website. Currently it is necessary to provide:

i.   toilet facilities clean, ventilated and properly lit (male and female);

ii. washbasins with hot and cold or warm running water (large enough to wash forearms properly), soap and towels or other drying facilities;

iii. changing facilities (male and female as appropriate) including areas for drying wet clothing and storing clothing;

iv. clean drinking water and a supply of cups or a water fountain.

v. a clean, warm place where workers can sit, make hot drinks and prepare and heat food. It should be equipped with seating with backs.

First aid arrangements should be in place according to current legislation and first aid boxes provided at suitable locations.

The location of first aid boxes and of the trained first-aiders should be clearly displayed at strategic places (e.g. canteen) and form part of Induction information.

When planning the layout of facilities consider issues such as:

i. setting up near site entrance to avoid visitors, delivery vehicles etc. from having to cross the site to get to the offices and welfare facilities;

ii. vehicle routes to segregate vehicles and pedestrians where practicable;

iii. access onto and from the site for vehicles and pedestrians

Thought should also be given to safety items such as a supply of posters, a hazards board, which is regularly updated, and information board containing information such as first aid and facilities, accident book location and how to get to the nearest hospital. The health and safety law poster must be displayed in a location where the entire workforce has access.

For more information on the welfare requirements of CDM 2007, see Annex M.

j) CONTROL OF ACCESS

The principal contractor is responsible for the safety of the site and is therefore responsible for taking reasonable steps to prevent unauthorised access to the site and putting people at risk. Unauthorised persons could also cause damage or interfere with the workplace in such a way as to create risks to themselves and to workers.

Special consideration should be given where there is a likelihood of children attempting to access the site. Sites located near to schools, play areas and high density residential areas need to be particularly aware of risks to children.

Sites may be fully hoarded, be fenced or (in the case of refurbishments etc.) have access points such as windows made secure.

For sites such as road works, a practical view needs to be taken so that if it is not practical to effectively secure the whole site, then areas where risks exist such as excavations, compounds and fuel points are secured.

High-risk areas such as High-Voltage rooms, lift motor rooms, cranes, hoists etc must be 'properly controlled'. It may be advisable to have 'permit to enter' and 'permit to work' systems for the safety sensitive areas.

k) SITE RULES

Principal contractors must prepare and then subsequently enforce site rules.

Any rule must be reasonable and wherever possible agreed with others on site.

Site rules can only be enforced if properly communicated and it is suggested that they are posted somewhere convenient (such as the canteen/rest room), included in starter information for new contractors and explained at site inductions.

As an example, site rules may include:

   i.   access points;

   ii. incident reporting;

   iii. rules on smoking;

   iv. rules on radios, iPods etc.;

   v. rules on parking;

   vi. consultation methods etc.

   vii. drugs and alcohol policy

l) PASSING ON INFORMATION

Principal contractors must provide copies of the relevant parts of the construction phase plan and site rules to anyone who needs it (including client, designers and visitors). It should be given in sufficient time for others to be able to brief their staff and to ensure that the information can be integrated within their own plans.

Providing the CDM co-ordinator with copies of changes to the plan as it is updated is a good way of keeping them in touch and allowing him to fulfil his duties.

m) DESIGN CHANGES

The principal contractor is in charge of the site during the construction phase. There is, however, likelihood that in many sites, designs will develop after initial construction work has commenced as specialists are identified and input into the design. There is also the possibility of client led changes requiring design changes. In these circumstances, the CDM co-ordinator has a role to satisfy himself that the design development meets the requirements of the duties of designer and CDM co-ordinator. It must however be clearly understood that the principal contractor is responsible for managing site activities and control of all parties contracted to him.

The principal contractor may opt to set up a meeting, involving the CDM coordinator, once it is apparent that ongoing design will be taking place. The main contact between CDM co-ordinator and any sub-contractors employed via the principal contractor (including designers in designbuild forms of contract) must be via the principal contractor who is responsible for the construction phase.

Where the designers are employed by the client, the CDM co-ordinator may deal directly but recognise their duty to co-operate with all parties. In particular they should involve the principal contractor so as to minimise the possible impact of the changes with possible commercial as well as health and safety implications. Changes need to be properly planned and adequate time allowed to consider any changes required to risk assessments and to method statements. Remember that it may not only be the trade or area of the site where changes are taking place which may be impacted by change and thought needs to be given to adjacent trades and work areas as well as impact on access requirements.

If temporary works are required, the CDM co-ordinator has a duty to see that they have been managed so as to ensure the safety of people who may be affected (including members of the public where applicable). The method of working chosen and the design of the temporary works remains the responsibility of the principal contractor and any of his sub-contractors who may be involved. The CDM co-ordinator does not have to check design calculations, but to satisfy himself that robust systems, managed by competent people, are properly in place.

n) HEALTH AND SAFETY FILE

Whilst it is the CDM co-ordinator's duty to compile the health and safety file, there is a duty on the principal contractor to promptly provide any information which is reasonably required.

It is good practice to agree the format and draft layout of the health and safety file as early as possible and, if possible, before starting work. Much of the information required will need to be provided by contractors, sub-contractors or suppliers and it is easier to get that information whilst they are on site rather than chasing for information at the end of the project where the subcontractors and suppliers may have left the site and prove difficult to contact or motivate.

Thought should be given to the structure of the file in instances such as practical completion of part of the work during the overall contract. In this case, consideration needs to be given to compiling sections of the health and safety file so as to be able to give to the client should he commission further work such as shopfitting. There may also be instances where a project has one initial client but may have several people requiring a file for their section.

A developer carrying out roadworks which form part of his development but which are eventually adopted by a local authority is an example of this where a stand-alone section of the file needs to be prepared to eventually be handed on to the local authority adopting the road. In a similar way, developments such as a multi-unit retail park needs to consider that retail units are likely to be handed over for fit out before the whole contract is completed and hence each unit will need a separate file ready for its practical completion.

Items that could be reasonably expected to be required in a health and safety file are shown in Annex F.

o) INDUCTION AND TRAINING

It is the principal contractor's responsibility to ensure that all workers have been provided with suitable health and safety induction, information and training.

The principal contractor will have a duty to provide suitable health and safety training for his own directly employed workers but not necessarily have to provide such training for contractors or sub-contractors he employs upon the contract. However, he will need to include consideration of such training when assessing the competence of companies and the people working for them.

The principal contractor does have the duty to ensure that everyone on site does have a project specific induction, and to be satisfied with the content of the contractors' induction material if additional contractor-specific inductions are given.

Inductions are best given by a senior member of the principal contractor's project team to demonstrate commitment and to allow the inductions to be a two-way process, giving feedback to a senior member of staff who is in a position to act on it.

There is a need for input from contractors and sub-contractors when their workforce is being inducted to ensure that they are aware of the safe system of work for their scope of work, are fully aware of equipment to be used etc.

Inductions should consider the potential impact of an activity upon other traders and on members of the public when carrying out their own activities.

A schedule of items to be covered in induction is given in Annex H.

p) WORKFORCE INVOLVEMENT

The principal contractor has a duty, in common with all of the other CDM dutyholders, to co-operate. The form of liaising with all other dutyholders needs to be clearly identified and agreed prior to the start of the project. Notes of any agreement or meeting content should be kept.

In particular, there is a duty for the principal contractor to involve and consult with the workforce. The principal contractor shall make and maintain arrangements which will enable him and the workers engaged in the construction work to co-operate effectively in promoting and developing measures to ensure the health, safety and welfare of the workforce.

Suggested methods of consultation are listed in Annex I.

q) LEGAL NOTICE

It is the duty of the principal contractor to ensure that a properly completed project notification poster is displayed in a prominent place (e.g. canteen) or places for a large project. The poster may be purchased from commercial suppliers such as Construction Industry Press or by laminating a copy of the F10 form.

4. WHO DOES WHAT, WHEN (see additional poster)

5. ANNEXES

ANNEX A - THE MANAGEMENT OF HEALTH AND SAFETY
Main Aims
The main aims of an occupational health and safety management system are to:

i.   Prevent accidents/incidents and other health and safety failures
ii. Enable planning for health and safety such as resource issues and training needs
iii. Ensuring occupational health and safety issues are integral to the day-to-day decision making

The practical objectives of safety management are:

i.   Gaining support for the health and safety effort
ii.   Motivation, education and training
iii. Achieving hazard and risk control by design and purchasing policies
iv.   Operation of a suitable inspection programme
v.   To ensure that hazard control principles form part of supervisory training
vi.   Devising and introducing controls based on risk assessments
vii. Compliance with regulations and standards

The key elements of a successful health and safety management system have been outlined in HS(G) 65:

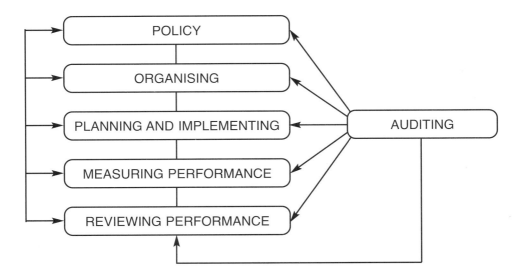

POLICY

Effective health and safety policies set a clear direction for the organisation to follow. Successful safety management demands comprehensive health and safety policies which are effectively implemented and which are considered in all business practice and decision-making. There must be clear accountability of the policy and safety management approach.

ORGANISING

An effective management structure and arrangements are in place for delivering the policy. Organisations that achieve high standards in safety create and sustain a culture that motivates and involves all members of the organisation in the control of risks.

PLANNING AND IMPLEMENTING

There is a planned and systematic approach to implementing the health and safety policy through an effective health and safety management system – to minimise risks. This ensures that the health and safety efforts really work. The following planning systems will help to achieve this

   i.   Identify objectives and targets which are attainable and relevant

   ii.   Set performance standards for management and control of risks which are based on hazard identification and risk assessment and which take legal requirements as the accepted minimum standard

   iii.   Consider and control risks both to employers and others and the structures they construct and complete

   iv.   Ensure documentation of all performance standards

MEASURING PERFORMANCE

Performance is measured against agreed standards to reveal when and where improvement is needed.

There are two types of monitoring systems:

   i.   Active Monitoring System – intended to measure the achievement of objectives and specified standards before things go wrong. This involves regular inspection and checking to ensure that standards are being implemented and that management controls are working properly.

   ii.   Reactive monitoring systems – are intended to collect and analyse information about failures in health and safety performance when things go wrong. This involves learning from mistakes.

Information from both active and reactive monitoring systems should be used to identify situations that create risks and enable something to be done about them.

AUDITING AND REVIEWING PERFORMANCE

The organisation learns from all relevant experience and applies the lessons. Auditing complements the monitoring programme and assesses the organisation's ability to meet its own standards.

The two main objectives of an audit are:

i.   To ensure that standards achieved conform as closely as possible to the objectives set out in the organisation's safety policy and

ii. To provide information to justify carrying on with the same strategy or a change of course.

Another way of reviewing performance is through benchmarking. This is a process of comparison with other similar organisations in terms of methods and systems used and also their cost savings and other results from using the systems.

Successfully implementing the health and safety management system

Successful implementation of the system needs the commitment from the following:

i.   Line management – including directors

ii.   Occupational health and safety is an integral part of business performance

iii. Legal compliance

iv.   Continual improvement

v.   Adequate resource allocation

vi.   Setting objectives/targets

vii. Effective planning processes

In both general management of health and safety and underlying CDM 07 – 5 key issues underpin organising for health and safety management:

i.   Control – right allocation of responsibilities and managers leading by example.

ii.   Co-operation – from everyone within the organisation and on the project

iii. Communications- all forms of communication which could affect behaviour of all those involved by providing information about hazards, risks and preventive measures

iv.   Competence – the selection, placement and training and instruction of all those involved

v.   Co-ordination – how all work together to the agreed objectives - both internally and externally between projects, sites, departments and other operating areas

A good safety record and documented safety management system cam more than repay the time spent on it because of its value in gaining new business. Many clients and project management operations have extensive vetting procedures to identify those contractors and suppliers who are competent in safety matters.

Establishing Cultural and Behavioural Change

Directors and other senior representatives within organisations are responsible for setting the tone and direction of the organisation's approach to health and safety. They have to ensure that health and safety risks are properly managed.

When a business starts out it is usual that they will seek compliance with the law as the first basis. The systems used to deliver compliance can be rudimentary and perhaps borrowed from others – but over time they will become established, adapted and continually reviewed to fit within the organisational approach.

Developing health and safety strategies is relatively straightforward but ensuring 'buy in' from the workforce is more challenging. Establishing a positive corporate culture around health and safety within an organisation is not simple. However the benefits of achieving this are significant – ensuring that the system, culture and aspirations of the business are so engrained and embedded within the management and workforce that they instinctively work safely and irrespective of their job title will challenge anyone else who appears not to subscribe to the company's ideals and standards of behaviour.

Transparency, excellent communication throughout the management structure and workforce, respect for one another, a no-blame and open culture linked to a sharing of experiences are hallmarks of an organisation that is looking to achieve a long standing positive culture.

Success in this area requires a high level of clearly evidenced management commitment at all levels. People are generally influenced by their bosses and therefore the actions of directors are very important in influencing and bringing about change. This is relevant to both large and small businesses.

The standards expected from everyone in the business should be written down in a one-page statement that can then be provided to those either within the organisation or working on the project. This is important as it sets the standard against which peoples' behaviour can be measured and provides the basis for action if appropriate.

Directors should consider how they can engage at site level with the workforce. Directors and senior managers could visit sites and ask the workforce what it is like to work on site and whether for example they feel 'safe'. They should also regularly ask senior manager how they are implementing their health and safety policy and how they monitor the workers' behavioural response to the policy.

A positive culture is hard to create and easy to lose. Building one will take time and will be the product of many small incremental actions. The mechanisms required to move an organisation into ensuring behavioural change will depend on the culture and management practice of the organisation. This can be a challenge when a company does not directly employ the entire workforce. By being open and honest about the cultural expectations and communicating this at all levels through the supply chain will help to effect change and create a belief that this is the way we do things round here'. This positive approach leads both to higher health and safety and commercial standards.

Behaviour-based safety

Measuring the frequency of safe behaviour generates more and more accurate predictive data and allows for precise reinforcement and provides positive accountability. The general principle involves sampling, recording and publicising the percentage of safe (versus unsafe) behaviours noted by observers from the workforce.

Employers investing in these techniques say they have found that the involvement of workers in the measuring process generates interest and improved commitment to employer's safety objectives. The techniques are said to lead to a reduction in loss-producing incidents as well as to the improved assessment of performance by the positive step of measuring workers' safe actions.

ANNEX B - PRINCIPLES OF PREVENTION

Regulation 7 CDM 07

When considering what precautions are necessary to control risks associated with a project, everyone who has a duty under CDM 07 to take account of the general principles of prevention specified in Schedule 1 to the Management of Health and Safety at Work Regulations 1999.

Effective planning is concerned with prevention through identifying, eliminating and controlling hazards and risks. The need for risk control within the construction industry is particularly important because of the high-risk nature of the work and the reliance on a significant number of contractors and subcontractors.

Eliminating risk is always the preferred approach where possible which requires substituting the dangerous substance or work practice by one which is not or less dangerous. This is followed by combating the risk at source by engineering controls and giving collective measures a priority. Measures include remote operated vibrating machinery or machinery guarding. Finally you should seek to minimise risk where the two other approaches are not possible by using for example personal protective equipment (PPE).

The General Principles of Prevention

Dutyholders should use these principles to direct their approach to identifying and implementing precautions that are necessary to control risks associated with a project.

i. IF POSSIBLE, AVOID THE RISK ALTOGETHER BY ELIMINATING THE HAZARD

It is always more effective to remove a problem altogether rather than to establish a control strategy, especially one which relies upon people to work in the correct way. This shows the importance of design and planning in safety management.

For Example: Do not specify fragile roofing materials through which people can fall – this is clearly more effective that specifying solutions designed to minimise the risks from falls through fragile material.

ii. EVALUATE THE RISK WHICH CANNOT BE AVOIDED BY CARRYING OUT A RISK ASSESSMENT

Risk assessments are carried out to enable control measures to be identified. These could be generic assessments or specific assessments depending on the tasks and nature of the risk involved.

iii. COMBAT RISKS AT SOURCE

Combating the risks at source rather than taking control measures that reduce the risk . Design and specification can make a significant difference to site conditions.

For Example: Designing floor slabs with fewer voids removes the need to control the risk of falling through them by setting up barriers or covering them. Avoid dust-producing processes by specifying off-site finishing

iv. ADAPT TO THE INDIVIDUAL

This is especially as regards the design of workplaces, the choice of work equipment and the choice of working and production methods, with a view, in particular, to alleviating monotonous work and work at a predetermined work-rate and to reducing their effect on health. Thought given to layout can improve working conditions and reduce risks.

For Example: Locating equipment such as a saw bench in a corridor could block access for others, may cause lighting difficulties and allow offcuts to pile up, increasing the risks. Asking how much room a carpenter needs and planning a suitable spot for a powered saw bench take little time.

v. USE TECHNOLOGY TO IMPROVE CONDITIONS

Technical progress often offers opportunities for improving working methods and making them safe

For Example: Use of low vibration hand tools or quieter machines. Use of a wheeled manhole lifter to replace hand hooks minimises the chance of back injury.

vi. DEVELOP COHERENT PREVENTION POLICY

This should cover technology, organisation of work, working conditions, social relationships and the influence of factors relating to the working environment – this will reduce those risks that cannot be prevented or avoided altogether.

vii. GIVE PRIORITY TO PROTECTION FOR THE WHOLE WORKPLACE RATHER THAN TO INDIVIDUALS.

Reliance on PPE as a sole means of risk control is rarely acceptable. This is because no PPE is 100% effective for 100% of the time for 100% of the people who use it.

For Example: Extensive work on a flat roof carried out by a number of workers from different employers – you should provide perimeter barriers rather than by giving everyone a safety harness. Installing permanent edge protection during the main construction process instead of at the end gives protection to both constructors and end users.

viii. ENSURE EVERYONE UNDERSTANDS WHAT THEY HAVE TO DO TO BE SAFE AND HEALTHY AT WORK

Safety awareness and worker instruction including induction is required on sites to make sure that everyone knows what the hazards and control measures are.

For Example: Specific site induction must include the local emergency evacuation procedure and understanding may need to be confirmed by holding regular practice fire drills.

ix. ESTABLISHING A POSITIVE HEALTH AND SAFETY CULTURE

Make sure that health and safety management is accepted by everyone and that it applies to all aspects of the organisations activities. Establishing a positive health and safety culture so that the avoidance, prevention and reduction of risks at work must be accepted as part of the organisation's approach to health and safety.

For Example: Failure of a senior manager to wear safety footwear and/or helmet on site visits gives the impression to the workforce that the rules do not apply to senior management.

Experience suggests that in a majority of cases, adopting good practice will be enough to ensure that risks are sufficiently reduced. More information on prevention is included in Annex B – The Principles of Prevention.

Preventing and controlling health risks

The principles for controlling health through risk assessment are the same as those for safety. However unlike safety risks that can lead to immediate injury, the results of daily exposure to health risks may not become apparent for a long time. Health may be irreversibly damaged before the risk is apparent and it is therefore essential to develop a preventive strategy to identify and control risks before anyone is exposed to them. Such measures help to sustain a healthy workforce and also prevent financial losses for the company through sickness absence, lost production, compensation and increased insurance premiums.

Examples of risks to health within the construction industry include:

i. Skin contact with irritant substances leading to dermatitis e.g. cement

ii. Inhalation of respiratory sensitisers e.g. silica dust

iii. Heavy, awkward and repetitive lifting leading to musculoskeletal problems e.g. lifting blocks, pile cap removal

iv. High noise levels causing deafness and tinnitus from e.g. road breaking, plant and machinery

v. High vibration levels e.g. from hand held tools such as breakers, compactors leading to hand arm vibration and circulatory problems

vi. Exposure to radiation including ultraviolet in the sun's rays causing burns, sickness and skin cancer

vii. Infections ranging from minor sickness to life-threatening conditions caused by inhaling or being contaminated by micro-biological organisms e.g. legionalla or weil's disease

viii. Stress causing mental and physical disorders from for e.g. lack of time to carry out tasks

There is much that can be done to prevent or control the risks to health by taking measures such as:

i. Talking to suppliers of substances, plant and equipment about minimising exposure e.g. low vibration tools, chromate free cement

ii. Specifying mechanical lifting for laying of kerbs or specifying low weight blocks

iii. Consulting the workforce on working practices to agree any design changes to working areas

iv. Ensuring workers are informed and trained about correct use of PPE where necessary such as ear defenders and gloves

Benefits of Risk Prevention

i. THE COST IN HUMAN SUFFERING

Physical pain and hardship resulting in death and disability is impossible to quantify. Many lives are lost through construction activities each year with thousands of injuries and cases of ill health. We know that construction safety is not an impossible dream; it is an achievable goal.

ii. MORAL

This stems from a developing public awareness that something needs to be done to raise the quality of life at work. It is morally unacceptable to put the safety and health of others at risk for profit or any other reason.

Worker morale is strengthened by active participation in accident prevention programmes and it is weakened by accidents. Adverse publicity affects the fortunes of the organisation.

iii. LEGAL

As outlined in the statute law. From this there is the threat of prosecution or other enforcement action as a consequence of failure to comply. Civil law enables injured parties to gain compensation. The cost in terms of money and adverse publicity can be very high, and there is the potential for a prison sentence in some circumstances.

iv. FINANCIAL

To ensure the financial health of a business and avoid the costs associated with accidents such as loss to employers, damage to property and production delays. Not all costs are insurable. This includes the cost of compensation – increased premiums will be a consequence of claims so there is an increase in overheads through direct costs.

Indirect costs include:

- Uninsured property and material damage
- Delays
- Overtime costs
- Time spent on investigations
- Fines
- Loss of expertise/experience

ANNEX C - COMPETENCE
General

It is key for CDM 2007 to work as intended that dutyholders who are appointed have the correct competences, are properly trained to carry out their duties and have sufficient resources available to them. No contractor, for example can be employed to carry out or manage construction work unless the person employing him or her is satisfied as to his or her competence.

In assessing competence, there should be focus on the needs of a particular project. Assessments must be proportionate to the risks, size and complexity of the work. The assessments must be realistic and not an unproductive paper chase. Also importantly the key message in the CDM is that making decisions on competence is a matter of judgement. There are no prescribed indicators of competence and a judgement must be made as to whether the core criteria have been achieved.

For small companies, the assessment should show to be simple and straightforward and they should be able to show that they meet the criteria without the need for extensive paperwork. Similarly for smaller projects companies should only be asked to provide the minimum paperwork necessary to show that they meet each element set out in the core criteria.

To be competent, an organisation or individual must have:

i.   Sufficient knowledge of the specific tasks to be undertaken and the risk which the work will entail

ii.   Sufficient experience and ability to carry out their duties in relations to the project and recognise their limitation and take appropriate action in order to prevent harm to those carrying out construction work, or those affected by the work

Development of "competence" is an ongoing process. Individuals will develop their competence by experience and training. Where appropriate, individuals should sign up to a "continuing professional development" programme to remain up to date with legislation, technical changes and good practice.

Everyone should receive some form of refresher training or training updates through in-house training or more formal skill-based training programmes such as those offered by ConstructionSkills.

Assessing Competence
An assessment of the company or organisation

It is necessary to undertake an assessment of the company or organisation's experience and track record to establish that it is capable of carrying out the specific work it seeks to do.

Stage 1: An assessment of the company's organisation and arrangements for health and safety to determine whether these are sufficient to enable them to carry out the work safely and without risk to health.

Stage 2: An assessment of the company's experience and track record to establish that it is capable of doing the work; it recognises its limitations and how these should be overcome and it appreciates the risks from doing the work and how these should be tackled.

Companies should be able to demonstrate that they have the ability to carry out the work safely and with due consideration to health. Remember that assessments should focus on the needs of the particular job and be proportionate to the real risks arising from the work.

Evidence should be properly focused. Unproductive bureaucracy can obscure the real issues and be a waste of time and effort.

It is recommended that companies produce evidence to demonstrate:

i. Their Health and Safety plan

ii. Their Health and Safety document

iii. Their arrangements for managing Health and Safety. These should identify duties under CDM 2007 and any other relevant legislation (e.g. Work at Height). There should be a clear indication of how arrangements are communicated to other parties

iv. The methods of determining training needs and meeting those needs identified

v. Details of qualifications and relevant expertise for key people (Board members, key Project Staff, safety team members as examples)

vi. Monitoring and Audit arrangements (including any external audit bodies)

vii. How the Workers are consulted and involved

viii. Arrangements for accident reporting and investigating accidents to avoid repeat occurrences

ix. Arrangements for ensuring that providers in the supply chain (suppliers and subcontractors) are able to carry out their duties safely and with regards to health and safety

x. How the company will identify significant Health and Safety risks and how they will be managed

Thought should also be given to other matters that may be relevant to the project being considered. These may include examples of good co-operation and co-ordination and examples of welfare facilities provided on previous contracts and welfare facilities proposed for the project being considered.

An assessment of the competence of individuals

As organisations, assessing the competence of an individual should be a two-stage process:

Stage 1: An assessment of the person's task knowledge to determine whether this is sufficient to enable them to carry out the work safely and without risk to health

Stage 2: An assessment of the individual's experience and track record to establish that they are capable of doing the work; they recognise their limitations and how these should be overcome and they appreciate the risks from doing the work and how these should be controlled.

Stage 1 assessments will look at the training record and qualifications of an individual. It will also probe if any arrangements are in place for continuing professional development or lifelong learning to ensure skills are kept up to date.

Issues to consider could include a simple record of relevant projects and the role that the individual carried out. A list of contacts who can confirm that the individual had carried out the competently would be of assistance. Where there are shortfalls identified, an explanation of how these shortcomings will be overcome should be furnished

Stage 2 assessments should concentrate on the person's past experience in the type of work that you are asking them to do. Where the work is more complex than any that the person has done before, or where the work will expose them to new risks, this should not automatically rule them out for consideration for the work. In these circumstances, the assessor should look for an appreciation of these risks; an understanding of how they will be managed, and some indication of how any shortcomings in their current knowledge will be addressed. Working under the supervision of someone who is competent and familiar with the work is one way in which people can learn how to do work safely.

Assessing an individual's basic understanding of site risks

A basic understanding of the general risks arising from construction work is essential underpinning knowledge for everyone who works in the industry in order that they can protect their own health and safety and understand the effect that their own actions could have on others. This is particularly important for those who will regularly visit or work on construction sites. This basic understanding should be the foundation for health and safety knowledge and understanding on which more detailed competencies are developed.

The Construction Skills touch screen test and equivalent schemes such as that offered by the Construction Clients National Certification Scheme are designed specifically to test this basic knowledge and understanding. Passing the touch screen test or equivalent schemes is one way of demonstrating this basic knowledge and understanding. All those who work on or regularly visit sites (including individuals from client, designer or CDM co-ordinator organisations) should be able to demonstrate that they have achieved at least this level of understanding before starting work on site.

Those who are new to construction work will need close supervision by an experienced person until they can demonstrate that they are aware of these risks and know how to avoid harm.

Assessing the competence of designers/CDM co-ordinators

When carrying out an assessment for designers or CDM co-ordinators, membership of a relevant construction-related professional institution gives a strong indication that the person has the necessary task knowledge and experience needed to fulfil the role. Some institutions have different levels of membership that may give a clearer indication of the knowledge that they possess.

Fellowship of an institution generally indicates that a member has more indepth knowledge and experience of a subject than that held by an ordinary member. Membership of a particular register operated by an institution also helps to indicate areas in which a person has particular expertise, for example membership of the Health and Safety Register operated by the Institution of Civil Engineers (ICE), membership of the design register or CDM coordinators' register operated by the Association for Project Safety (APS), or membership of the CDM co-ordinators' register administered by the Institution of Construction Safety (ICS) (formerly the Institution of Planning Supervisors (IPS)).

Competence of individual designers

Membership of a relevant professional institution for example CIBSE; ICE; IMechE; IStructE; RIBA; RICS; CIAT; CIOB is a strong indicator that a designer has the necessary task knowledge and an ability to recognise the health and safety implications of their design work. Membership of a relevant register administered by such an institution gives a more detailed indication that the designer has the necessary knowledge and experience, for example the Construction Health and Safety Register of the ICE, or the design register operated by the APS.

Those who specify materials, equipment and standards of finish (for example interior designers) are also considered designers under the Regulations, but they tend not to be members of specific professional institutions. Relevant academic qualifications or evidence of their past experience in this type of work will give a strong indicator as to their competence. Those who only occasionally become involved with design work and who do not meet the qualifying criteria (for example trainees) should work under the supervision of a competent designer.

When carrying out Stage 2 of the assessment you should consider the designer's past experience in the type of work that you are asking them to do. Those without relevant experience should be allowed to work under the supervision of someone who has it. If designers work as part of a team, different individuals may bring different skills and knowledge to the work, and this should be taken into account when making the assessment.

Assessing the competence of individual CDM co-ordinators

CDM co-ordinators need good interpersonal skills in order to encourage co-operation between designers and others. Although there is a legal duty to co-operate on everyone involved with the project, the CDM co-ordinator has a specific duty to ensure that co-operation happens. Without it, good working relationships, clear communication and sharing of relevant information will not happen. An over-bureaucratic approach should be avoided, not least because it makes it harder to secure the co-operation that is needed.

CDM co-ordinators also need a sound understanding of:

i.   health and safety in construction work;

ii. the design process;

iii. the importance of co-ordination of the design process, and an ability to identify information which others will need to know about the design in order to carry out their work safely.

This knowledge needs to be relevant to the project and future maintenance, use, refurbishment or demolition of the structure. The size and complexity of the project will determine whether an individual is capable, and has the resources to carry out all of the work required.

CDM co-ordinators are not necessarily designers, and do not have to undertake any design work themselves. But in order to assess the health and safety implications of the design, they must have sufficient knowledge of the design process to enable them to hold meaningful discussions with designers, recognise when information about risks arising from the design will need to be passed to others and participate fully in relevant design team meetings. They will also need to be in a position to advise clients about the competence of others who are appointed by the client, and be able to assess whether the construction phase plan prepared by the principal contractor is adequate for controlling the risks associated with the project.

When carrying out the assessment, clients will need to take into account the size and complexity of the project, and the nature of the risks that will be associated with it. Where one individual does not possess all of the skills and experience necessary, the work can be shared with others, but it must be clear who is responsible for each part of the work, and who is in overall control.

For small projects where there are no special risks, Stage 1 of the assessment should concentrate on the person's knowledge of the construction processes and the health and safety risks associated with the work. An appropriate health and safety qualification such as a NEBOSH construction certificate will demonstrate that the person has adequate knowledge of health and safety, but this will need to be coupled with a Stage 2 assessment to demonstrate that they have experience in applying this knowledge in the construction environment.

Registration on the CDM co-ordinators' register administered by the ICS (formerly the IPS) or the APS or membership of the Health and Safety Register administered by the ICE can be taken as confirmation that the person has the necessary task knowledge and experience to carry out the CDM co-ordinator's duties on this type of project.

For larger or more complex projects, or for those with unusual or higher risks, the skills and knowledge of the CDM co-ordinator will need to reflect the complexity of the project and the specialist knowledge necessary to ensure that risks are properly controlled. It is more likely in these circumstances that a corporate appointment will be made and the competence assessment will be made against the core criteria.

CDM co-ordinators cannot carry out their duties effectively without the client's support. For that reason they will often need an understanding of relevant aspects of the client's business and the implications of the proposed work for it. CDM co-ordinators will need to make sure that clients understand their own role and duties as well as the benefits of good management of the project and early appointment of dutyholders.

Assessing the competence of an individual site worker

Employers are required by law to ensure the competence of their employees and to provide training and instruction as necessary. CDM2007 places duties on contractors and principal contractors to ensure that workers are competent and to provide training where necessary.

An appropriate Skills for Business Organisation, or similar programme give a good indication of this basic knowledge and understanding. This should be the foundation for health and safety knowledge and understanding on which more detailed competencies are developed. Having gained this basic knowledge and understanding, workers should then receive regular updates and more specialised training as part of a life-long learning process. This should either be delivered through a planned programme of 'on-the job' training, for example through regular on-site 'toolbox' talks coupled with 'off-the-job' training days, or through a more formal, assessed training package, for example an S/NVQ programme administered by an appropriate Skills for Business organisation, or similar programme.

Workers who follow the 'in-house training' route to competence will need to ensure that the training they receive covers the health and safety aspects of the job as well as the necessary skills elements. Those who enroll on an accredited S/NVQ course will receive both elements of the training as part of the assessed course.

Unskilled workers who are following a programme of training will, over time, gather the necessary competence to become a skilled worker. With further experience and training, they should gain the competence necessary to become a supervisor.

When developing training schemes, it is important to ensure that the content and style are appropriate. This includes providing training in a form that trainees can understand. Workforce or trade union appointed safety representatives can make a significant contribution to developing such training, and a joint approach can help ensure people adopt good practices.

Information and training should be provided in a way that takes account of any language difficulties or disabilities further advice is provided by CILT, the National Centre for Languages (www.cilt.org.uk) and the Construction Confederation (www.thecc.org.uk). It can be provided in whatever form is most suitable in the circumstances, as long as it can be understood by everyone. For employees with little or no understanding of spoken or written English, employers need to make special arrangements. These include providing translation, using interpreters, and replacing written notices with clear symbols or diagrams.

ANNEX D -PRE-CONSTRUCTION INFORMATION

The client, owner of structures and others may hold valuable information that may help prevent accidents or instances of ill-health occurring. Examples will include the asbestos register and information on services (wiring, drawing, routing of gas pipes etc.)

The client may also have requirements that they may require the contractors to observe whilst working on their projects. This will be particularly relevant if work is being carried out in premises that are still occupied by the client. In this case, there may be specific requirements on issues such as parking, access, use of radios etc.

The pre-contract information is the place to ensure that this key information is available to those who will be bidding to carry out the work. Some of the information will be required by designers (e.g. which walls are known to be load-bearing and details of services) and should be made available before significant design commences.

The pre-construction information should be considered by those parties bidding for work to ensure there are no "surprise requirements". The information should also be considered when the principal contractor is drawing up his construction phase plan. Only relevant information should be included.

Pre-construction information should include:

Description of the Project

  i.   Key dates, including planned start and finish dates and any phased handover requirements
  ii. The minimum time to be allowed between appointing the principal contractor and commencing work on site
  iii. Detail of client, designers CDM Co-ordinator and other stakeholders (e.g. nominated subcontractors)
  iv. Noting if Workplace (Health, Safety and Welfare) Regulations 1992 apply
  v.   Extent and location of existing records and plans – to included any soil surveys or ground investigation

Client Consideration and Management requirements

The client's consideration should include any specific requirements they may have. This is particularly important where the client occupies the structure whilst construction work is carried out. The client may also have specific requirements for image and cleanliness (e.g. when constructing a new place of a partly occupied business park). Client management should include:

  i.   Arrangements they may require for managing the works – including any health and safety goals

ii. Requirements for communicating and reporting

iii. Any specific requirements for hoardings, signs and branding

iv. Any transport, vehicle routing and parking requirements

v. Any client permit to work requirements, including limitations on time and noise etc.

vi. Existing fire precautions

vii. Existing emergency procedures and means of escape

viii. Any areas designated as confined spaces

ix. Any specific client requirements and restrictions such as smoking and use of radio's

Existing Risks

Safety hazards, including:

i. Boundaries and access such as narrow routes or storage problems

ii. Adjacent land uses such as schools, railways lines etc.

iii. Any known hazardous materials on site

iv. Location of all services. A survey should be carried out if practicable rather than leaving it to the Principal Contractor and Contractors.

v. Information on existing structures such as stability (load bearing walls pre-stressed concrete members, stress skin roofing etc.)

vi. Any anchorage points for fall arrest systems

vii. Any structured alterations, including fire damage and ground shrinkage or subsidence

viii. Any health and safety information including as-built drawings

Health hazards, including:

i. Asbestos

ii. Existing (or past) storage areas for hazardous land

iii. Health issues arising for client alterations

Significant design and Construction Hazards

i. Significant design assumptions – particularly where the need for the Temporary Works has been identified

ii. Arrangements for design development and changes – including keeping the relevant CDM dutyholder involvement

iii. Information on significant risks identified during design work

iv. Materials requiring particular percentages

The Health and Safety File

A description of how the client wants the file to be structured (see Annex F on Health and Safety file)

ANNEX E - THE CONSTRUCTION PHASE PLAN

Under Regulation 3 of the Management Regulations, the principal contractor and other contractors must identify the hazards and assess the risks relating to their work, including the risks they create for others. Using this information, the principal contractor must develop a plan suitable for managing health and safety in the construction phase of the project and including developing information provided by the client and CDM co-ordinator.

The construction phase plan is the foundation for good management and clarifies:

    i.   who does what?

    ii. who is responsible for what?

    iii. what hazards and risks have been identified

    iv. how shall the works be controlled

Under CDM, it is the responsibility of the principal contractor to develop the construction phase plan once they have been appointed. In doing so, the principles of risk prevention must be followed.

The plan must be completed before the client can allow work to proceed on site. For all but the simplest projects, it is likely that the plan may not be sufficiently developed to cover all of the work the project will involve but may only cover early phases of work (e.g. site set up, enabling works, clearance and early groundworks). The plan at this phase should, however, indicate how arrangements for managing the rest of the work will be added into the plan as contractors and sub-contractors are identified and can give meaningful input into their part of the plan.

The plan should be regarded as a live document, reviewed at regular intervals and, where necessary, amended to reflect changes in scope of work or programme changes where the planned interface of trades may alter.

The principal contractor's plan should be in proportion to the risks involved and structured to reflect the following information.

Construction phase plan
Description of project

    i.   project description and programme details including any key dates;

    ii. details of client, CDM co-ordinator, designer, principal contractor and other consultants;

    iii. extent and location of existing records and plans which are relevant to health and safety on site.

Management of the work

    i.   management structure and responsibilities;

ii. health and safety goals for the project and arrangements for monitoring and review of health and safety performance;

iii. arrangements for:
  - regular liaison between parties on site;
  - consultation with the workforce;
  - the exchange of design information between the client, CDM co-ordinator and contractors on site;
  - handling design changes during the project;
  - the selection and control of contractors;
  - the exchange of health and safety information between contractors;
  - site security;
  - site induction;
  - identifying needs and arrangements for competent training;
  - welfare facilities and first aid;
  - the reporting and investigation of accidents and incidents including near misses;
  - the production and approval of risk assessments and written systems of work;

iv. site rules including client requirements;

v. fire and emergency procedures.

Arrangements for controlling significant site risks

Safety risks including:

i. delivery and removal of materials (including waste) and work equipment taking account of any risks to the public, e.g. during access to or egress from the site;

ii. services, including temporary electrical installations;

iii. preventing falls;

iv. work with or near fragile materials;

v. control of lifting operations;

vi. dealing with services such as Water, electricity, gas, communications cabling etc.;

vii. the maintenance of plant and equipment;

viii. poor ground conditions or contaminated ground;

ix. confined space working;

x. demolition;

xi. managing temporary works;

xii. traffic routes and segregation of vehicles and pedestrians including access onto and from site;

xiii. storage of materials (particularly hazardous materials) and work equipment;

xiv. dealing with existing unstable structures;

xv. accommodating adjacent land use;

xvi. any other significant safety risks.

Health risks:

i.   the removal of asbestos;

ii. dealing with contaminated land;

iii. manual handling;

iv. use of hazardous substances, animal hazards (such as rats – leptospirosis);

v.   reducing noise and vibration;

vi. any other significant health risk such as dust.

The health and safety file

i.   layout and format;

ii. arrangements for the collection and gathering of information;

iii. storage of information;

As contractors and sub-contractors are identified and sub-contractors let, their information should be incorporated in a form which can dovetail into the plan.

Constant review is key and the principal contractor should allow the CDM coordinator access to review meetings in order to demonstrate that both parties are fulfiling their duties to communicate and co-operate.

ANNEX F - THE HEALTH AND SAFETY FILE
General

The Health and Safety file is only required under CDM for notifiable projects. However, clients on non-notifiable projects may choose to include a requirement for information similar to the file when letting contracts.

The object of the Health and Safety file is to store information needed to allow future construction work (including cleaning, maintenance alterations, refurbishments and demolitions to be carried out safely. Information in the file should alert those doing the work to the risks and help them plan safe systems of work. The file should be specific to the Project and not contain any unnecessary generic matter.

It is essential that the structure and content of the file must be agreed between the client and the CDM co-ordinator at the start of the project. In particular, thought needs to be given on how information can be retrieved when needed. It is good practice to ensure that the principal contractor and contractors are aware of the requirement for the H&S file at the time projects are being priced so that the information can be gathered in a structured manner whilst people are on site rather than gathering information in a poorly co-ordinated rush at the end of the project.

Thought should be given to the needs for the File and the timing for producing it where there may be several ultimate clients on a single project.

Example – A developer builds a retail park. To access the site he needs to do major works on a trunk road and also improvements to the local road network. Ultimately, separate Files will be needed for each party.

 i.   The Highways Agency for the trunk road
 ii. The Local Authority for local roads
 iii. Each Retail unit as it is sold and fitted by new owner
 iv. The common areas

The individual H&S files should be available at the time of handover

What you must do

For notifiable projects:

 i.   CDM co-ordination must prepare, review, amend or add to the file as the Project progresses. They must be aware of when the client will need it.
 ii. Other dutyholders must co-operate to provide the information required by the File to a reasonable timescale.
 iii. Clients must retain the File safely and make available to those who will need it for future work. Note:
 iv. The File should contain only relevant material and not burdened with

material which is of no use

v. Whilst it is the duty under the Regulations for the CDM Co-ordinator to compile the File and hand it to the client, a pragmatic view should b taken when collecting the information. In some forms of contract it may be more practical for the Principal Contractor to collect information, in all cases, responsibilities and timetables should be made clear at the earliest possible stage in the Project.

vi. Remember that it may prove difficult to obtain information after designers or contractors have completed their work and have left the Project

The Contents of the File

When putting together the Health and Safety file, you should consider including information about each of the following where there are relevant to the heath and safety of any future construction work. The level of detail should allow the likely risks to be identified and addressed by those carrying out the work:

i. A brief description of the work carried out

ii. Any residual hazard which remain and how they have been dealt with (e.g. surveys or other information concerning asbestos; contaminated land; water bearing strata; buried services etc);

iii. Key structural principles (e.g. Bracing, sources of substantial stored energy – including pre or post tensioned members) and safe working loads for floors and roofs, particularly where these may preclude placing scaffolding or heavy machinery there;

iv. Hazardous material used (e.g. lead paint, pesticides, special coatings which should not be burnt off etc)

v. Information regarding the removal or dismantling of installed plant and equipment (e.g. any special arrangements for lifting, order or other special instruction for dismantling etc)

vi. Health and safety information regarding the removal or dismantling of installed plant and equipment (e.g. any special arrangements for lifting, order or other special instructions for dismantling etc.)

vii. Health and safety information about equipment provided for cleaning or maintaining the structure

viii. The nature, location and markings of significant services, including underground cables; gas supply equipment; firefighting services etc;

ix. Information as –built drawings of the structure, its plant and equipment (e.g. the means of safety access to and form service voids, fire doors and compartmentalisation etc)

The file does not need to include things that will be of no help when planning future construction information, or construction phase plan such as:

i.   The pre-construction information, or construction phase plan

ii. Construction phase risk assessments, written systems of work and COSHH assessments

iii. Details about the normal operation of the completed structure

iv. Construction phase accident statistics

v.   Details of all the contractors and designers involved in the project (though it may be useful to include details of the Principal Contractor and CDM Co-ordinator)

vi. Contractual documents

vii. Information about structures, or part of structures, that have been demolished – unless there are any implications for remaining or future structures

viii. Information contained in other documents, but relevant cross-references should be included.

Storing and Use

i.   The file needs to be kept up to date and retained for as along as it is relevant – normally the lifetime of the structure.

ii. Storage can be electronic (with back-up), on paper (but remember photocopies fade with time), on film or any other durable format.

iii. When clients dispose of their interest in a structure, they should pass the file to the new owner

iv. If the structure is being managed by others on behalf of the client, it is essential that the information is available to them

v.   If the client leaves the building or lets it out to tenants with cleaning and repair duties, the relevant parts of the file must be made available

vi. In multi-occupancy situations (e.g. a block of flats), relevant information should be available to those cleaning and maintaining the works. Also, individual occupiers should be supplied if there is information relating to the areas, which they occupy.

ANNEX G – CONTRACTS

CDM and the different contracts

There are many different ways of procuring construction projects and a large number of forms of contract have been developed to allow clients to procure work with contracted relationships and risk profiles to meet their needs.

CDM 1994 was designed to cater for procurement via 'conventional' contract form where a client would engage a design team to carry out design which, when well advanced, would allow him to appoint a contractor to construct the project. Since then, procurement methods and contractual relationships between the parties have developed as design-build procurement has developed onwards into PFI/PPP (Private Finance Initiative/Public, Private Partnerships). Forms of procurement and new risk sharing concepts such as NEC, have been developed.

Several forms of contract may alter relationships where designers may be appointed by contractors. In some cases the CDM role may move to another party as in the case of PFI contracts where the original client will hand over his role to an SPV (Special Purpose Vehicle) once the contract has reached an agreed stage of development.

No matter which form of contract is chosen, there are a number of underlying principles which must be considered when structuring the contract to the project.

i. It must be structured to allow CDM to function so that ALL duties are carried out at ALL times.

ii. In order to achieve i, each party must clearly understand which CDM role they are carrying out at all points in the life of the project.

iii. Parties must agree and clearly communicate which CDM duty falls to them to carry out. In particular:

- Who is to notify HSE
- Who is to prepare the pre-construction information
- Who is to prepare the construction phase plan
- Exactly what the client will be expecting from the CDM co-ordinator.

Duties and responsibilities should be clearly developed as sub-contractors are brought into the scheme.

Sub-contractors forms of procurement must mirror the main contract provisions.

Robust systems must be agreed and implemented to ensure that the parties to the contract recognise and carry out their CDM duties. It is possible to consider how the dutyholder may change during the course of a project and structure arrangements accordingly.

As an example: -

A developer wishes to build a retail park which requires access via a new bridge over a major highway, minor roadworks to be adopted by the local authority and a number of retail units to be purchased by the retail companies. In this instance the original client will evolve into a number of clients during the course of the work.

i. The developer will be the principal client and may have a role as designer if they have input into the specification or client.

ii. He may retain ownership of common areas and require a health and safety file for areas he will control.

iii. The Highway Authority procures the bridge via the developer but may have a role as designer if they require work done to their specification. At the end of the project they will adopt the bridge and require a health and safety file for it.

iv. The local authority procures work via the developer but may have a role as designer via their input to specification. At the end of the project they will adopt the roadworks and require a health and safety file.

v. The retailers may have involved their own specification and/or designers to the shell of the retail shed which they procure via they developer and hence may be deemed to have a role as designer.

Once the retail sheds are substantially complete, the developer will hand them over to the retailer who will become the client for the ongoing fitting-out work and will appoint his own principal contractor to carry out this work and his own CDM co-ordinator.

The developer's CDM co-ordinator will need to prepare a health and safety file for the retail shed and hand it on to the retailer prior to work commencing on the fit-out and the retailer's team will add to the health and safety file.

Whilst this may appear complex, considering who does what for the whole life of the project will facilitate smooth running and avoid wasted effort. Making sub-contractors of the developer's principal contractor aware that the information they provide for the retail shed will need to be capable of being broken down into individual sheds will enable him to plan this in advance.

Many of the more recent forms of contract such as NEC (New Engineering Contract) are based upon the principles of working together, and embracing the ideas in the recent 'Accelerating Change' report.

The key CDM principles of co-operation and co-ordination lie at the heart of these forms of risk-sharing and trust based contract. They tend to have lead in periods which give time to consider risks, commercial as well as health and safety, and to work together to derive optimum solution for the whole life of the project.

Private Finance Initiative (PFI) and PPP (Private, Public Partnership) contracts also depend upon co-operation from all parties to arrive at the best overall solution to meet the client's requirements. In these forms of Contract there is usually a long lead-in period between the initial concept and work commencing on site. If used well, this period can be used to develop cost saving value engineering along with the possibility of innovation and the opportunity to design-in health and safety measures before work starts on site. Many times this produces a win-win situation where safer and healthier methods have proved to be cost-effective in the long-term life of the project.

In PFI and PPP contracts, the role of the client will almost certainly change.

The project originator is the client until someone else takes on this role, so they should ensure that there are appropriate arrangements for managing the project. This includes ensuring that the roles of all those involved in the project are made clear at all stages, and that adequate time and resources are available to ensure health and safety throughout the project.

To meet the aims of CDM it is crucial that early designs and specifications take full account of the requirements of the designer and design work. If this is left until a contract is awarded it may be too late. Addressing these issues at such a late stage is likely to be ineffective and expensive.

Project originators are responsible for any requirements they impose. This may make them designers under CDM, with the additional duties of a designer. They must provide any relevant information to inform the designer, and ensure that a pre-construction information is provided to bidders. A Special Purpose Vehicle, once appointed, normally takes over as the client for the remainder of a project.

ANNEX H – INDUCTIONS

Introduction

Whether you are on a site which is notifiable under the CDM Regs or not, whether your company is the principal contractor, the main contractor, a contractor, sub-contractor or an organisation having a visiting or other resident professional role; all people on site need to have some form of induction by the site manager or his delegate.

The safety policy of each employer should define the standard of induction training that will be given. The main purpose is to impart four key areas of information, namely; Site Rules, Emergency Arrangements, Welfare Arrangements and information relating to any particular, significant or unusual hazards which exist.

Format

It is common for people to undergo inductions in a group and in a room close to the site which has been organised to facilitate the site induction process, however inductions have been successfully conducted by walking those being inducted around and showing them. This approach has been used particularly effectively when inducting those with limited understanding of written & spoken English.

Approach

Since the site induction is often the first time many operatives meet a particular site manager then the induction should be used to set the right tone of co-operation required from all on site whilst also setting the scene of intolerance towards those who do not co-operate.

A participative approach is preferable to a dictatorial one and an enthusiastic efficient induction rather than a style which portrays the presenter as bored and only there because he's told to do them, would also result in the messages being better received. Therefore, improving the presenters' style and selecting the right person to giving the inductions is a key starting point.

The site induction is not a training session but an information passing session and should therefore not need to be overly long. Flip charts and presentation folders can be usefully used whereby the presenter uses crib notes on the rear or the presentation pages as his prompt whilst the inductee is viewing something more pictorial. Asking questions of those being inducted is recommended to determine their understanding of information needing to be imparted. Induction aids are available from various sources including ConstructionSkills.

Content

A generic content is contained on the next page which can be adapted to suit the largest or smallest site.

Records

It is advisable to maintain records of those who have been inducted along with a copy of what information was covered in the induction. Induction training could for example be recorded in a log or register and may be connected to the issue of identity badges.

Site Health and Safety Site Induction Content

i.   Introduction
   - E.g. welcome, a description of what the project is about & who's it for, how important is safety and who's who.
   - The general requirements and approaches of the principal contractor and the client

ii.   What are the Site Rules
   - E.g. Reporting of accidents, demonstrating training & competence, wearing safety equipment, receiving a briefing on your safe system of work, hand-over of documentation such as permits to work, rules on access and parking, use of radios and mobile phones.

iii.   What are the Site Emergency Procedures
   - e.g. Medical, Fire, other

iv.   What are any particular current hazards
   - Live gas mains, overhead cables, asbestos, clients' activities

v.   What are the welfare arrangements
   - e.g Toilet locations/messrooms/drying rooms

vi.   Where people can go for assistance/further information/help
   - e.g Office, notice board, worker safety reps, complaint lines

vii.   What will happen to those who don't co-operate
   - e.g. Red/yellow cards, 3 strikes & out, company disciplinary procedure.

ANNEX I – WORKER CONSULTATION

Introduction

Worker Engagement is a process where every worker on a construction site actively participates in improving health and safety by influencing others. More specifically, workers are keen to share their experience and knowledge with other workers and managers; managers positively encourage worker participation to identify and resolve health and safety problems, and everybody on site benefits from safer working conditions. Sites where workers are engaged are generally safer than those where they are not.

The construction industry is unusual because the co-operative approach required for successful engagement extends not only to employees of a single employer but also all the people working on a site or project, regardless of their employment status.

Legal drivers for worker engagement

The following are the key legal drivers for worker engagement:

i. The Safety Representatives and Safety Committee Regulations (1977) place duties on employers to consult and provide facilities and assistance to Trade Union appointed Safety Representatives, where a Union is recognised and has made appointments, and confer rights on Safety Representatives to carry out certain specified functions.

ii. The Health and Safety Consultation with Employees Regulations 1996 (HSCER) place duties on employers to consult with employees, who are not represented by Trade union Safety Representatives on matters relating to their health and safety at work.

iii. In the construction industry, relatively few sites have active Union appointed Safety Representatives, or elected Representatives of Employee Safety under the (HSCER). The third route prescribed by law is for the employer to consult directly with employees.

iv. The Construction Design and Management (CDM) Regulations 2007 place a specific duty on Principal Contractors to ensure that all workers on the site are consulted on matters connected with the project which may affect their health and safety. Therefore, the Principal Contractor's duty to consult extends to all workers on site, regardless of who their employer is. A separate regulation requires everybody involved in the construction work to co-operate, to establish and maintain high standards of health and safety provision.

There are also good business reasons for worker engagement. Interaction can lead to improvements in technical knowledge throughout any organisation or project team. Feedback from workers can also be used to check management performance, increase productivity, efficiency and motivation levels as well as lower workforce turnover.

Principal Contractor Approach

The principal contractor has a duty to co-operate with the workforce and to see that they are consulted on matters to health and safety on a project.

Equally, the workforce has a duty to co-operate with management and all others on the project. Particular worker duties are scheduled later in this annex.

Consultation may be carried out directly by the principal contractor or by the Contractor who is the direct employer. In the case that the consultation is carried out via the contractors the principal contractor must be satisfied that meaningful consultation is being carried out. In Particular, he must be aware of any comments relating to adjacent activities of other contractors and act to manage problems identified.

Consulting with the workforce can be effective in a number of ways, depending on a number of factors including:

   i.   is there a union presence on site;
   ii. what is the size of the site and the size of the workforce;
   iii. the tasks to be undertaken, and the risks associated with such tasks;
   iv. the turnover of the workforce so as to keep continuity of consultation and ensure representation from all of the trades and contractors.

Whilst there may be formal committee structures in place on large projects, this may not suit simple sites with few people. Regular informal meetings in a tea break can often work well and help getting a positive contribution.

Other pro-active methods can include a "working well together walkabout" where representatives of all of the trades working on site to regularly carry out a "walkabout" recording issues which may be of concern and actively seeking to agree improvement which are practical and cost-effective. It is essential that where agreement on actions has been reached then the agreement is clearly made public and the agreed actions are taken and are seen to be taken. This method addresses the major problem of trade turnover and worker turnover during the life of a project.

Workers should be consulted by their employer when Method Statements are drawn up so they agree to work to that method, fully understand the method and the health and safety issues arising. In particular they need to agree and be aware of the correct plant and equipment to use and any PPE that may be required for the tasks to be carried out. The principal contractor needs to be fully satisfied that this process is in place and that any Method Statement takes account of adjacent and interfacing activities. Should the worker have reservations or wish to input into better or safer methods then they need to inform management or supervisors.

An agreed system needs to be put in place to allow **anyone** to notify management in the event of serious and imminent danger to persons at work. In particular workers need to be made aware of their right to stop work and move to a place of safety. The induction must include a section letting workers be aware of how to contact managers in the case of emergencies and letting them know their rights.

The induction is also the best way to inform workers how to input ideas or concerns outside of any formal process, committee etc. which may have been put in place.

Toolbox talks, well presented, are another means of creating a dialogue but must be delivered as a two-way process, inviting comment and ideas.

On large sites, separate methods of consultation may be needed for individuals, gang/trade groups and whole Project. Details can be found on the Health and Safety Strategy pages of the Major Contractors Group webpage.

As noted, workers have a duty to co-operate and their duties may be summed up as below.

Workers Duties:

i.   To co-operate with the employer and follow any information, instructions and training that they are given

ii.   Not interfere with or misuse anything which the employer has provided in the interests of health, safety and welfare

iii. To take reasonable care for their own health and safety at all times and to make sure that they do not endanger themselves or any other person

iv.   To use all tools and equipment safely and in accordance with instructions given or training received

v.   Report any defects or potential hazards in equipment to their supervisor as soon as possible

vi.   As regards manual handling, to make proper use of any safe system of work or mechanical means provided by the employer

vii. To only use or operate the tools, plant and equipment which they have been trained and are authorised to use

viii. Use the personal protective equipment supplied by the employer correctly, to take care of it and to report any loss or defects in the equipment

ix.   Not to erect, alter or dismantle any scaffolding unless competent to do so or under the supervision of a competent person

x.   When operating goods hoists, to keep the gates closed except when loading or unloading, not to over-ride any controls, not to allow any passengers

xi. Do not block or obstruct any access or means of escape

xii. Make full use of any control measures provided to prevent or limit exposure to substances hazardous to health, and to wear or use any personal protective equipment provided

xiii. Not to use a mobile elevating work platform for any purpose other than as a work platform

xiv. Co-operate with Health and Safety Executive Inspectors, as required

xv. Not to remove safety guards or render inoperative any safety device fitted to any plant or equipment

xvi. Not to ride on plant or vehicles unless authorised to do so and in a proper seat

xvii. Recognise the importance of personal cleanliness, especially when working with substances harmful to the skin

xviii. Never to exceed the safe working load of any equipment

xix. Report to the supervisor all accidents that cause any injury

xx. Understand and comply with all signs and notices that are displayed

xxi. Wear ear protectors in designated areas where mandatory warning signs are displayed

xxii. Do not carry out any repairs, especially not electrical repairs, on any plant or work equipment, unless authorised, and competent to do so

xxiii. To follow all company and site health and safety rules.

ANNEX J – FAQ'S

A web version of this document, which will be regularly updated and revised, will be available at the CDM pages of the HSE Construction website (www.hse.gov.uk/construction).

General

Q1. What are these regulations about?

Q2. Is CDM 2007 mainly a revision of CDM 1994?

Q3. Do the Regulations apply to all construction projects?

Q4. When is a construction project "notifiable"?

Q5. Does the 30 days include weekends, bank holidays etc?

Q6. What if a project is already underway?

Q7. What actually comprises a construction project?

Q8. What about Part 4 of CDM 2007?

Q9. How does CDM 2007 encourage better worker engagement?

Q10. Can a single project take place on different sites or at different locations?

Q11. Can a person or organisation discharge more than one CDM 2007 duty?

Q12. What about demolition?

Clients

Q13. Do the Regulations apply to projects with a domestic client?

Q14. Why is a domestic client not a 'client' under the CDM 2007?

Q15. Do I have to notify a project which is for a domestic client and which lasts more than 30 days, or more than 500 person days of work?

Q16. Do projects with a domestic client and which last longer than 30 days, or 500 person days of construction work, require a CDM co-ordinator, a principal contractor and a health and safety plan?

Q17. If I am a contractor working on a project for a domestic client, do I have to comply with CDM 2007?

Q18 If I am a designer working for a domestic client, do I have to comply with CDM 2007?

Q19. As a client, what do I have to do to comply with regulation 9 of CDM 2007?

Q20. As a client, what should I be looking for as suitable arrangements for managing the project?

Q21. Does CDM 2007 apply to self-build projects?

Q22. Does CDM 2007 apply to the client of a "live/work" unit?

Q23. Does CDM 2007 apply to property developers?

Q24. Does CDM 2007 apply to a management company owned by the residents/homeowners of a block of flats?

Q25. What is this 'new duty' on clients?

Q26. Is Reg 9 CDM a new duty?

Q27. What about clients with no knowledge of construction work? Surely they will need to appoint a consultant to help them for even the smallest project?

Q28. Does this mean clients carrying out detailed checks, and getting involved in the construction work itself?

Q29. What about larger projects? Surely these are too complex for clients to know what is needed

Q30. What is meant by "reasonable steps" and "suitable arrangements"?

Q31. Can a client still appoint a 'client's agent'?

Q32. Why was the 'clients agent' provision removed from CDM 2007?

Q33. Does this mean a client can no longer appoint someone else to meet the client's duties on their behalf?

Designers

Q34. Am I a designer?

Q35. Can you summarise what I should be doing as a designer?

Q36. Does CDM 2007 apply to designers?

Q37. Do designers have any additional duties if the project is notifiable?

Q38. What is 'initial design work'?

Q39. Am I a designer if I only review the designs of others on behalf of the client?

Q40. What would be reasonable for me to do to ensure that the client will be aware of his duties under CDM 2007?

Q41. I'm a bit confused about whether I should be using Design Risk Assessments, Design Risk Reviews, or some other means of documenting my risk procedures. Can you help me?

Q42. I thought the Management of Health and Safety At Work Regulations 1999 (MHSWR) required risk assessments, so why don't I have to do specific design risk assessments?

Q43. Why do I have to know about construction techniques and methods? That's what the contractor does.

Q44. Are there any transitional arrangements for designers, when the revised regulations come into force?

Q45. How and what information should designers pass on?

Q46. Do designers need to eliminate all risks?

Q47. What do you mean by 'a project advisor'?

CDM co-ordinators

Q48. The CDM co-ordinator is a new role, so what are the main duties of CDM co-ordinators?

Q49. Who can be a CDM co-ordinator

Q50. Is the CDM co-ordinator the same as the old planning supervisor?

Q51. Will existing planning supervisors need more training if they are to become CDM co-ordinators?

Q52. What do you mean by 'a project advisor'?

Q53. When should the CDM co-ordinator be appointed?

Q54. Can a CDM co-ordinator be a company or an individual?

Q55. Should the CDM co-ordinator monitor site conditions?

Principal Contractors

Q56. What are the main duties of the principal contractor?

Q57. I have a small building company, and sometimes I act as principal contractor on a project, and sometimes as a contractor or even sub-contractor. Have any of my duties changed under CDM 2007?

Q58. As a Principal Contractor, when do I have to prepare a construction phase plan for health and safety on the site?

Contractors

Q59. Have contractors' duties changed under the revised regulations?

Q60. What if the job is not notifiable, and there is no principal contractor?

Q61. Reg 13(6) requires contractors to prevent unauthorised access to sites, and Reg 27(2) requires sites to be identified with signs and/or fenced off. Isn't this the same thing?

Pre-Construction Information

Q62. As a client, do I still have to provide information about the site to contractors who I am thinking of appointing to carry out the work?

Q63. As a client, do I have to provide information about asbestos, which may be present in the structure

Q64. What should a client provide as pre-construction information?

The Plan and File

Q65. What is the difference between a Construction Phase Plan and a Health and Safety File?

Competence

Q66. I have heard that competence is now a key issue in CDM 2007. Why is this?

Q67. How can I assure the competence of my site-based workforce?

Training Material

Q68. Will HSE be producing any training material to assist my company in training key personnel for CDM 2007?

Enforcement of CDM 2007

Q69. Will CDM 2007 still just be enforced by HSE inspectors?

General

Q1. What are these Regulations about?

A. CDM 2007 is about focusing attention on effective planning and management of construction projects, from design concept onwards. The aim is for health and safety considerations to be treated as a normal part of a project's development, not an after thought or bolt on extra. The object of the regulations is to reduce the risk of harm to those that have to build, use and maintain structures.

Q2. Is CDM 2007 mainly a revision of CDM 1994?

A. Firstly, Parts 1, 2 & 3 of CDM 2007 deal with similar issues as CDM 1994 on how construction projects should be managed and organised to ensure health and safety. However, the requirements have been streamlined and improved and there are therefore some differences. Secondly, the existing Construction (Health, Safety and Welfare) Regulations 1996 are completely revoked and have now been incorporated as Part 4 of CDM 2007, with little change. Part 4 of CDM 2007 deals mainly with health, safety and welfare requirements on site during the construction phase.

So the previous 2 sets of regulations are now combined into one package, called CDM 2007.

Q3. Does CDM 2007 apply to all construction projects?

A. CDM 2007 applies to all construction projects where people are at work. The Regulations are divided into five parts:

    i. Part 1 deals with the application of the Regulations and definitions.

    ii. Part 2 covers general duties that apply to all construction projects.

    iii. Part 3 contains additional duties that only apply to notifiable construction projects, i.e. those lasting more that 30 days or involving more than 500 person days of construction work.

    iv. Part 4 contains practical requirements that apply to all construction sites.

    v. Part 5 contains the transitional arrangements and revocations.

Q4. When is a construction project "notifiable"?

A. A project is notifiable to the HSE if the construction phase will be longer than 30 days or 500 person days of construction work (projects for operational railways will be notifiable to the Office of Rail Regulation). Guidance on how to notify projects, and the F10 form that can be used, is on the HSE Construction website (www.hse.gov.uk/construction).

Q5. Does the 30 days include weekends, bank holidays etc?

A. Any day on which construction work takes place is counted. What matters is how many days of construction work the project entails, not when these days occur.

Q6. What if a project is already underway?

A. The new Regulations will apply to projects that are already in progress. There are a number of provisions to aid the transition from the old duties to the new e.g. a planning supervisor or principal contractor already appointed under CDM 94 will be deemed to be the CDM co-ordinator or principal contractor under CDM 2007, but they must ensure that they acquire the new competencies within 12 months, if necessary. Part 5 of CDM 2007 deals with transitional arrangements.

Q7. What actually comprises a construction project?

A. A project is not only the construction work, but also includes all the planning, design, and management or other work until the end of the construction phase. It also includes subsequent maintenance, alteration or demolition of a structure or building.

Q8. What about Part 4 of CDM 2007?

A. Part 4 of the Regulations contains the duties to control specific worksite risks which were formerly contained as provisions in the Construction Health Safety and Welfare Regulations 1996. For example, requirements on safe working near excavations, during demolition and dismantling, while working with explosives and maintaining safe access to and from places of work are contained here.

Part 4 applies to all construction work and places duties on any person carrying out construction work, or any person under the control of a person carrying out construction work.

Q9. How does CDM 2007 encourage better worker engagement?

A. Reg 24 places a duty on principal contractors to make and maintain arrangements to enable effective co-operation between all parties on site, and to consult with all workers on site. Consultation means not only giving information to workers but also listening and taking account of what workers say, before making health and safety decisions. Part of the purpose of consultation is to ensure that the measures taken on site to protect workers health and safety are effective.

Principal contractors are encouraged to develop a variety of methods of communication and consultation with the workforce, to develop collaboration and trust. When matters of concern are raised by workers these should be actioned, and feedback given to the workforce. Evidence that this is happening provides assurance that effective worker engagement is in place.

Involving the workforce in identifying and controlling risks is crucial in preventing accidents. Whether projects are notifiable or not, contractors have a duty in Regulation 13 to inform workers of their procedures for stopping work in the event of serious and imminent danger, and to provide training where necessary. This should ensure that workers are willing and able to intervene to prevent an accident sequence developing.

Q10. Can a single project take place on different sites or at different locations?

A. Yes. For example a single client may have several premises that are to be refurbished under the scheme (e.g. branches of a bank, Job Centres etc.), where the same designer, CDM co-ordinator, and principal contractor are to undertake the works at every premises. These can be treated as part of the same overall project, but an amended notification (Form F10) should be submitted to the relevant HSE area office giving details of the location of each site. Particular care will need to be taken to ensure that the client provides pre-construction information relevant for each location, and that the construction phase plan is suitable for each location.

Q11. Can a person or organisation discharge more than one CDM 2007 duty?

A.   Yes, an individual or company can discharge more than one CDM function provided they have the appropriate level of competence.   It is not necessary for individuals or companies with CDM duties to be independent of one another.   For example, clients may decide to discharge the co-ordination duties themselves or they may appoint the lead designer as the CDM co-ordinator. It is possible for all the duties to be discharged by the same company. However an appointment of a CDM co-ordinator and principal contractor for notifiable jobs must be made.

Q12. What about demolition?

A.   A plan detailing the arrangements for how demolition work will be carried out must be prepared before demolition or dismantling work begins. This applies to all demolition work regardless of size, duration or whether the job is notifiable. Demolition means the deliberate pulling down, destruction or taking apart of a structure, or a substantial part of a structure. Similarly, dismantling will be considered to be the taking down or taking apart of all, or a substantial part of a structure. Construction operations such as the making of openings for doors, windows, services or removing non structural elements such as, stripping cladding, removing roof tiles and similar operations is not considered to be demolition or dismantling in themselves. Where these operations are combined with other operations they may together form demolition and dismantling projects. The erection and taking down of a scaffold used for the purposes of construction is construction work. The striking of a scaffold will not be considered to be the demolition or dismantling of a structure.

CLIENTS

Q13. Do the Regulations apply to projects with a domestic client?

A.   Parts 1, 2, 4 and 5 of CDM 2007 apply to projects for a domestic client, but the domestic client has no duties. This is because domestic clients do not fall within the definition of a 'client' in Regulation 2(1). A domestic client is someone who lives, or will live, in the premises where the work is carried out.   The premises must not relate to any trade, business or other undertaking. Although a domestic client does not have duties under CDM 2007, those who work for them on construction projects will.

Q14. Why is a domestic client not a 'client' under the CDM 2007?

A. The definition of a client in Reg 2(1) of CDM 2007 states that:

'A client is a person who in the course or furtherance of a business-

    i.   seeks or accepts the services of another which may be used in the carrying out of a project for him, or

    ii. carries out a project himself'.

Since a domestic client does not have work done 'in the course or furtherance of a business', they are not classed as a client by CDM 2007, and therefore they do not have duties under the regulations.

Q15. Do I have to notify a project which is for a domestic client and which lasts more than 30 days, or more than 500 person days of work?

A. No. This is because Part 3 of the Regulations does not apply to projects carried out for a domestic client, so there is no requirement to notify the project.

Q16. Do projects with a domestic client and which last longer than 30 days, or 500 person days of construction work, require a CDM co-ordinator, a principal contractor and a health and safety plan?

A. No. This is because a domestic client is not a 'client' as defined by the regulations, and Part 3 of the Regulations does not apply to projects where there is a domestic client.

Q17. If I am a contractor working on a project for a domestic client, do I have to comply with CDM 2007?

A. Yes. You will need to comply with all of the duties that apply to contractors in parts 1, 2, and 4 of CDM 2007.

Q18. If I am a designer working for a domestic client, do I have to comply with CDM 2007?

A. Yes, you will need to comply with the duties placed on designers in parts 1 and 2 of the Regulations (there are no duties on designers in parts 4).

Q19. As a client, what do I have to do to comply with regulation 9 of CDM 2007?

A. Clear guidance on what clients need to do is given in the ACOP, and the Construction Clients' Group has produced additional industry guidance that is available. Clients need to check that:

i. Designers, contractors and other team members that you engage are competent, are adequately resourced, and appointed early enough for the work they have to do;

ii. You allow sufficient time for each stage of the project, from concept onwards;

iii. You co-operate with others concerned in the project to allow other dutyholders to comply with their duties under the regulations;

iv. You co-ordinate your own work with others involved with the project in order to ensure the safety of those carrying out the construction work, and others who may be affected by it;

v. There are suitable management arrangements in place throughout the project to ensure that the construction work can be carried out, safely and without risk to health. (This does not mean managing the work yourself, as it is unlikely that clients have the expertise and resources needed);

vi. Your contractors have made arrangements for suitable welfare facilities to be provided from the start and throughout the construction phase;

vii. Any fixed workplaces (e.g. offices, shops, factories, schools), which are to be constructed, will comply, in respect of their design and the materials used, with any requirements of the Workplace (Health, Safety and Welfare) Regulations 1992; and

viii. Relevant information likely to be needed by designers, contractors or others to plan and manage their work is passed to them.

Q20. As a client, what should I be looking for as suitable arrangements for managing the project?

A. You will need suitable arrangements to ensure:

i. Clarity of roles, functions and responsibilities for members of the project team, so everyone knows who does what;

ii. Those appointed by you have sufficient time and resource to comply with their duties;

iii. There is good communication, co-ordination and co-operation between members of the project team (e.g. between designers and contractors);

iv. Your designers are able to confirm that their designs (and any design changes) have taken account of the requirements of regulation 11 of CDM 2007 (designers duties), and that the different design elements will work together in a way which does not create risks to the health and safety of those constructing, using or maintaining the structure;

v.   Your contractors are provided with the pre-construction information; and

vi.   Your contractor is able to confirm that health and safety standards on site will be controlled and monitored, and that welfare facilities will be provided for the duration of the construction phase.

These arrangements should focus on the needs of the particular job and be proportionate to the risk arising from the work. They will mainly be made by others in the project team, such as designers and contractors. Before they start work, a good way of checking is to ask the relevant members of the team to explain their arrangements, or to ask for examples of how they will manage these issues during the life of the project. When discussing roles and responsibilities, on simple projects all that may be needed is a simple list of who does what.

Q21. Does CDM 2007 apply to self-build projects?

A.   This depends. If the project is one where a person is building their own domestic dwelling, which they intend to occupy, then there will be no CDM duties on the "self builder". Where the "self-builder" engages a designer for the project, then that designer will have the normal CDM designer duties. If the self-builder engages a contractor to assist him with the work, then that contractor will have a duty to carry out the work safely in accordance with their CDM duties as a contractor.

Where several "self-builders" group together to build their own homes, they may agree to help one another with the work.   Where a "self-builder" agrees to assist another (whether or not for profit) this amounts to an undertaking, and the "self-builder" offering his services should comply with the contractor duties.

Where a "self-builder" builds a house or structure with the intention of selling it, then this is an undertaking, and there will be client and contractor duties that apply to the "self-builder".

Q22. Does CDM 2007 apply to the client of a "live/work" unit?

A.   A "live/work" unit is partially a domestic dwelling, and partly a location for the carrying out of an undertaking (whether or not for profit). Where there is any element of a business or undertaking, then the client is no longer a pure "domestic client". The element of an undertaking means that the client will assume CDM client duties, even where they are "self-building".

Q23. Does CDM 2007 apply to property developers?

A.   Yes. Property developers are carrying out work in the furtherance of a business, and therefore they are 'clients' under the Regulations.

Q24. Does CDM 2007 apply to a management company owned by the residents/homeowners of a block of flats?

A. Yes. The management company is a business (whether for profit or not) and is classed as the client. All parts of the Regulations will apply where relevant.

Q25. What is this 'new duty' on clients?

A. CDM 2007 makes explicit, the duties which clients already had under the Health and Safety at Work Etc Act 1974 (HSWA) and the Management of Health and Safety at Work Regulations 1999. In summary, Regulation 9 of CDM 2007 requires clients to take reasonable steps to ensure that the arrangements made for managing the project (including the allocation of sufficient time and other resources) by persons with a duty under the Regulations, are suitable to ensure that the construction work can be carried out safely, and without risks to health.

Q26. Is Reg 9 CDM a new duty?

A. No. This duty was already implicit in the Health and Safety at Work etc Act 1974 and the Management of Health and Safety at Work Regulations 1999, and this was explained in the CDM 1994 Approved Code of Practice.

Q27. What about clients with no knowledge of construction work? Surely they will need to appoint a consultant to help them for even the smallest project?

A. No. For smaller sites with no special risks, the questions clients will need to ask are simple and straightforward:

    i.   They will need to make sure that the contractor has made arrangements to fence off the site and protect members of the public who may be affected by the work.

    ii.   They will need to check that contractors have arrangements in place for securing the health and safety of their workforce.

    iii. They will need to check that the contractor has made arrangements for welfare facilities.

    iv. They will need to make sure that designers have arrangements in place that will reduce risk arising from design decisions.

Q28. Does this mean clients carrying out detailed checks, and getting involved in the construction work itself?

A. No. Health and safety on site is a matter for the contractor, and the duty to reduce risks through design is a duty of the designer. Clients simply have to ensure that the initial project management arrangements that have been made are maintained. This can be achieved by seeking assurance from the designer and contractor. For a non-notifiable job, simple enquires will be enough to check that the arrangements are in place to ensure that:

i. There is adequate protection for the client's workers and/or members of the public; if appropriate for the project;

ii. Adequate welfare facilities have been provided by the contractor;

iii. There is good ongoing co-operation and communication between designers and contractors; and

iv. The management arrangements for the project, which the contractor agreed to make to control key risks on site, have been implemented.

You do not need to get involved with the day-to-day running of the project. There is no obligation for a client to visit the site. If you feel you need advice then it is likely to be available from the competent person you have appointed under the Management of Health and Safety at Work Regulations 1999.

Q29. What about larger projects? Surely these are too complex for clients to know what is needed?

A. For projects lasting longer than 30 days or involving more than 500 person days of construction work, clients must appoint a CDM co-ordinator whose primary function is to advise the client. The CDM co-ordinator will be able to advise the client on the appointment of competent duty holders; assessing the adequacy of other team member's management arrangements and assessing the adequacy of the health and safety plan. The client is entitled to rely on the advice of the CDM co-ordinator when making their judgements.

Q30. What is meant by "reasonable steps" and "suitable arrangements"?

A. This really depends upon the nature of the project. For a non-notifiable project (construction work not exceeding 30 days or 500 person days) then the answer in the Question above will be reasonable. Arrangements will be suitable if they are able to deal with health and safety hazards and risks, and provide suitable site welfare. For notifiable projects the CDM co-ordinator will advise the client. The CDM co-ordinator should be competent to take reasonable steps on behalf of the client to ensure the management arrangements are suitable. The nature of the project will determine this. A large housebuilding scheme will present different requirements to the construction of a road bridge over a working railway line, for instance.

What is NOT reasonable is for a client to appoint a contractor, and then make no enquiries at all about any arrangements for managing the health and safety of the project, either at the start or during the project. Clients are not permitted to be "oblivious" to the contractor's arrangements.

Q31. Can a client still appoint a 'client's agent'?

A.   No. Under CDM 1994 clients could appoint a 'client's agent' who would take on the duties and liabilities of the client. Under CDM 2007 clients can still engage someone to carry out their client duties on their behalf, but onus for compliance with the regulations stays with the client. This is the same as for any other health and safety regulation. However if a client's agent has already been appointed under the CDM 1994 then he/she may continue to act as client's agent for that project, if both parties agree, until such times as the project comes to an end, the appointment is revoked, or five years after the introduction of the new regulations, whichever comes first.

Q32. Why was the 'clients agent' provision removed from CDM 2007?

A.   Because it causes confusion. Appointing a 'client's agent' under CDM 1994 meant that the client's agent assumed the duties of the client in CDM 1994. However, clients also have duties under the Health and Safety at Work (etc) Act 1974 and under the Management of Health and Safety at Work Regulations 1999. Appointing a 'client's agent' did not relieve the original client of duties under other legislation. By removing the 'clients agent' provision in CDM 2007, this area of confusion and inconsistency is removed, and CDM 2007 is on the same footing as all other health and safety legislation.

Q33. Does this mean a client can no longer appoint someone else to meet the client's duties on their behalf?

A.   No. A client can still ask someone else to manage the construction work on their behalf and meet their duties as a client, but the client still remains liable for meeting the client duties. This is the same situation that applies to any other health and safety responsibility.

DESIGNERS
Q34. Am I a designer?

A.   A good question because the answer is not always obvious! Firstly, you have to be in a trade, business, or undertaking that involves you in preparing designs. In CDM the term "designer" relates more to the function performed, rather than the profession or job title. So, for a construction project there could be "traditional" designers, such as architects, structural engineers, and civil engineers, a design and build contractor etc. There will also be the less obvious designers, such as building services engineers/consultants, quantity surveyor etc.

You could also be a designer if you prepare drawings, specifications, and bills of quantities. The design of temporary works on site (often by contractors) would also be classed as design work.

Q35. Can you summarise what I should be doing as a designer?

A. The main designer duties under the Regulations are:

i. To make sure you are competent for the job in the first place.

ii. To check that clients are aware of their duties under the Regulations before you start work on the project;

iii. When preparing the design, avoid risks to those:

- Carrying out construction work.
- Liable to be affected by the construction work.
- Cleaning any window or transparent or translucent wall, ceiling or roof in or on the structure.
- Maintaining permanent fixtures and fittings of the structure.
- Using the structure as a workplace

When doing this, you should avoid hazards that may give rise to risks; and reduce risks from any remaining hazards.

iv. These duties should be performed so far as is reasonably practicable, taking account of other relevant design considerations.

v. Provide relevant information with the design about aspects of the design of the structure or its construction or maintenance, as will adequately assist clients, other designers, and contractors to comply with their duties under the Regulations.

vi. Take account of the Workplace (Health, Safety and Welfare) Regulations 1992

Q36. Does CDM 2007 apply to designers?

A. The general duties relating to designers apply to all construction work, whether or not the project is notifiable.

Q37. Do designers have any additional duties if the project is notifiable?

A. Yes. Where the project is notifiable, designers should not commence work (other than initial design work) unless a CDM co-ordinator has been appointed. They must also provide the CDM co-ordinator with any information about aspects of their design which will help them discharge their CDM duties, including information that may be needed for the health and safety file.

Q38. What is 'initial design work'?

A. 'Initial design work' includes feasibility studies to enable the client to decide whether or not to proceed with the project, and any work necessary to identify the client's requirements or possible constraints on the development. Designers should encourage the appointment of a CDM co-ordinator at the earliest opportunity.

The following examples illustrate what is beyond preliminary design, and hence that which should not be progressed in the absence of a CDM co-ordinator:

i.   Work within and beyond RIBA Stage C

ii. Work within and beyond CIC Consultant Contract 2006 Stage

iii. Work beyond OGC Gateway 1; and

iv. Work within and beyond ACE Agreement A (1) or B (1) 2002 Stage C3.

Q39. Am I a designer if I only review the designs of others on behalf of the client?

A. If you are carrying out the review as part of your business, then it depends what you do. If you make no amendments to the designs, and neither specify materials, methods of work, sequencing, etc, then the design remains unchanged and you have not become a designer. Stating that a design is unacceptable does not make you a designer, but requiring specific changes to a design does make you a designer.

Q40. What would be reasonable for me to do to ensure that the client will be aware of his duties under CDM 2007?

A. This depends upon the knowledge and experience of the client, and also the complexities of the construction project. As a designer, you need to have a knowledge of the client duties as they affect the project, so that you can give the client proper advice. You need to let the client know that you cannot begin work until you have made him aware of his duties. You also need to be reasonably satisfied that the client has understood the advice that you have given. This can be done verbally or in writing.

Q41. I'm a bit confused about whether I should be using Design Risk Assessments, Design Risk Reviews, or some other means of documenting my risk procedures. Can you help me?

A. The principal aim should be to eliminate hazards from the design (so far as is reasonably practicable), and reduce risks from any remaining hazards – giving priority to collective protective measures before individual protective measures. For most designers the consideration of hazard and risk is integrated within the design process, so there is no need to carry out a separate "design risk assessment". A design review may also be useful as a means of checking that the principle aim of eliminating hazards or reducing risks is achieved. However, there should be liaison with others who need to know the information about residual risks, so that relevant information is made available. Any paperwork should focus on significant residual risks, particularly those that may not be obvious to others.

A design practice or design team may choose to adopt their own procedures to make sure that designers are aware of their responsibility to eliminate hazards and reduce risks. The nature of these procedures will depend on the size of the design practice/team, and the type of work undertaken.

Q42. I thought the Management of Health and Safety At Work Regulations 1999 (MHSWR) required risk assessments, so why don't I have to do specific design risk assessments?

A. Reg 3(1) of MHSWR does require employers and the self-employed to make a suitable and sufficient assessment of risks to which their own employees are exposed at work, and also the risks arising out of, or in connection with, their work activity (e.g. designs) to which others may be exposed. The purpose of the risk assessment is to identify measures needed to comply with relevant health and safety law.

However, the risk assessment of a design should be integral to, and evolve with, the design work itself. Every design is different, and every design will require a degree of calculation, assessment, review, and the proper exercise of judgement. If a designer is complying with Reg 11 of CDM 2007, then as the design is worked through to completion any hazards will be eliminated and residual risks (to those who may be affected by them) reduced, so far as is reasonably practicable. This is, in effect, the application of risk assessment to the design. There is no legal requirement for a risk assessment to be in writing or recorded, however, Reg 3(6)(a) of MHSWR does require the significant findings of the assessment to be recorded where an employer employs five or more people. In terms of design, the significant findings of the assessment will usually be the finished design, together with all relevant drawings, and any accompanying notes.

Reg 3(3) of MHSWR requires any assessment to be reviewed if no longer valid, or if there have been significant changes. Most design practices already do this, by a systematic process of design review throughout the development of the design. Designers may choose to record the reasons why a design was modified or revised.

Para 113 of the CDM 2007 ACOP states that "compliance with Reg 11 of CDM 2007 will usually be sufficient for designers to achieve compliance with Regs 3(1), (2), and (6) of MHSWR as they relate to the design of the structure".

Q43. Why do I have to know about construction techniques and methods? That's what the contractor does.

A.   Yes, but designers need to have a basic understanding of how their designs can be built, maintained, and demolished. Without this basic knowledge, designers will find it difficult to eliminate hazards and reduce risks at the design stage. Where designers do not have this knowledge they will need to seek assistance, which may be available from specialists designers, consultants, or contractors.

Q44. Are there any transitional arrangements for designers, when the revised regulations come into force?

A.   No. Any design work completed prior to 6 April 2007 should comply with the requirements of CDM 1994. However, any design work that is completed on or after 6 April 2007 must comply with CDM 2007. This means designers should avoid foreseeable risks to persons using a structure designed as a workplace, and take account of the Workplace (Health, Safety and Welfare) Regulations 1992 relating to the design of, and use of materials in, the structure.

Q45. How and what information should designers pass on?

A.   Designers should inform others about project specific significant residual risks. This should focus on risks that may not be obvious to those who use the design. One good way of communicating this information is using notes on drawings, if you are not sure what information should be passed on talk to the CDM co-ordinator or contractor about what they need to know.

Q46. Do designers have to eliminate all risks?

A.   No. Designers should avoid hazards where possible, but there will be many situations where it is not possible to avoid all hazards. Where hazards cannot be avoided, the designer should reduce the risks associated with the hazard. The amount of effort put in to avoiding hazards and reducing risks should be proportionate to the degree of risk. They are not required to spend time, money and trouble on low risk issues.

Q47. What do you mean by 'a project advisor'?

A. Under CDM 2007, clients are required to make sure that other members of the project team have adequate arrangements in place to ensure the health and safety of those working on the project. The CDM co-ordinator has a duty to advise and assist the client in meeting this obligation. If the CDM co-ordinator is unhappy with the arrangements made by a particular project team member, they should advise the client of their concern. The client can then insist that the problem is put right. This means that the client empowers the CDM co-ordinator to ensure that the arrangements put in place by the project team are sufficient in health and safety terms.

CDM CO-ORDINATORS

Q48. The CDM co-ordinator is a new role, so what are the main duties of CDM co-ordinators?

A. The main duty of CDM co-ordinators are to advise and assist the client in meeting their duties as a client under the CDM 2007 and, in particular:

   i. the duty to appoint competent designers and contractors;

   ii. the duty to ensure that adequate arrangements are in place for managing the project;

   iii. notify HSE about the project;

   iv. co-ordinate design work, planning and other preparation for construction where relevant to health and safety;

   v. identify and collect the pre-construction information and advise the client if surveys need to be commissioned to fill significant gaps;

   vi. promptly provide in a convenient form to those involved with the design of the structure; and to every contractor (including the principal contractor) who may be or has been appointed by the client, such parts of the pre-construction information which are relevant;

   vii. manage the flow of health and safety information between clients, designers and contractors;

   viii. advise the client on the suitability of the initial construction phase plan and the arrangements made to ensure that welfare facilities are on site from the start; and

   ix. produce or update a relevant, user friendly, health and safety file suitable for future use at the end of the construction phase.

Q49. Who can be a CDM co-ordinator?

A. Anyone can be a CDM co-ordinator provided that they have the appropriate level of competence. The CDM co-ordinator can be a designer, contractor or a stand-alone co-ordinator. The task can be shared out and the role can be combined with another role for example project manager, designer or principal contractor. A formal appointment in writing must be made.

Q50. Is the CDM co-ordinator the same as the old planning supervisor?

A. No. Although the duties are broadly similar, CDM 2007 requires a very different approach from the old planning supervisor. The CDM co-ordinator is the facilitator that ensures that the project team co-operate and co-ordinate their work with respect health and safety and advises the client. The CDM co-ordinator, need different skills and competencies to make sure these duties are met. In particular, they must advise the client on how to meet the client's duties under CDM 2007, and assist them in doing so. The role of CDM co-ordinator provides the client with a project advisor on health and safety management, and ensuring effective planning of the work, to assist with the appointment of competent contractors, to ensure the proper co-ordination of the design process and to prepare the health and safety file.

Q51. Will existing planning supervisors need more training if they are to become CDM co-ordinators?

A. It depends on their existing competence. CDM co-ordinators must be competent for the duties that they are called on to perform. They will need good communications and inter-personal skills to fulfil their role. They will need to have a good understanding of the design and construction process and knowledge of health and safety. The transitional provisions in CDM 2007 allow 12 months for planning supervisors to acquire the new skills that they need (Part 5 of the regulations). If they have not achieved competence during that period, a new CDM co-ordinator will need to be appointed.

Q52. What do you mean by 'a project advisor'?

A. Under the CDM 2007 clients are required to make sure that other members of the project team have adequate arrangements in place to ensure the health and safety of those working on the project. The CDM co-ordinator has a duty to advise and assist the client in meeting this obligation. If the CDM co-ordinator is unhappy with the arrangements made by a particular project team member, they should advise the client of their concern. The client can then insist that the problem is put right. This means that the client empowers the CDM co-ordinator to ensure that the arrangements put in place by the project team are sufficient in health and safety terms.

Q53. When should the CDM co-ordinator be appointed?

A. The CDM co-ordinator should be appointed as soon as practicable after initial design work is completed. 'Initial design work' includes feasibility studies to enable them to decide whether or not to proceed with the project, and any work necessary to identify the client's requirements or possible constraints on the development. The CDM co-ordinator must be appointed early- because the role is crucial for the effective planning and establishment of management arrangements from the start of the project. The CDM co-ordinator must be appointed before detailed design work begins.

Q54. Can a CDM co-ordinator be a company or an individual?

A. Either. For many projects, particularly smaller ones, the CDM co-ordinator appointed by the client may be an individual person. For larger projects, the CDM co-ordinator is more likely to be a company / firm / partnership. In this instance it is acceptable for the name of the CDM co-ordinator on the notification to HSE to be that of the organisation.

Q55. Should the CDM co-ordinator monitor site conditions?

A. No CDM does not require the CDM co-ordinator to assess the performance on site of the principal contractor. The overall responsibility for controlling and monitoring site health and safety standards lies with the principal contractor.

PRINCIPAL CONTRACTORS
Q56. What are the main duties of the principal contractor?

A. The main duties of the principal contractor are to:
    i.   Plan, manage and monitor the construction phase to ensure, so far as is reasonably practicable, that it is carried out without risks to health or safety.
    ii. Ensure that there are adequate welfare facilities for those working on the site.
    iii. Draw up and implement the site rules.
    iv. Draw up and implement the construction phase plan.
    v.   Provide a suitable site induction and ensure that those working on

site have received the training that they need to carry out the work safely and without risks to health.

vi. Ensure the site is suitably fenced and prevent unauthorised people from entering the site.

vii. Ensure that there is co-operation between those working on the site, and that work is co-ordinated in such a way as to prevent danger.

viii. Ensure that there are suitable arrangements for effective consultation with the workforce.

ix. Make sure that the right health and safety information is provided to the right people at the right time.

x. I have a small building company, and sometimes I act as Principal Contractor for a project, and sometimes as a contractor or even subcontractor. Have any of my duties changed under CDM 2007?

Q57. I have a small building company, and sometimes I act as principal contractor for a project, and sometimes as a contractor or even sub-contractor. Have any of my duties changed under CDM 2007?

A. Nothing much has changed for you, although if you act as a principal contractor you are required to have arrangements for consultation with the workforce. You will probably find that the client asks you about your arrangements for the health and safety management of the project, and about your competence. You will also find the CDM 2007 ACoP useful in outlining the sort of checks you should make on your sub-contractor's competence. But if you were complying with the CDM 1994 and the Construction (Health, Safety and Welfare) Regulations 1996, then you should have no difficulties.

Q58. As a Principal Contractor, when do I have to prepare a construction phase plan for health and safety on the site?

A. You need to prepare the plan before the start of construction work, for all jobs that are notifiable. The plan should be specific to the particular site or project, and set out how you will manage the construction phase and the key health and safety issues for the particular project. Keep the plan relevant – it should be a practical aid to help you. There is more information about this in the Appendix 3 of the CDM 2007 ACoP. Although you don't need to have a written health and safety plan for non-notifiable projects, you will still need to plan and manage these aspects of the construction phase appropriately.

CONTRACTORS

Q59. Have contractors' duties changed under the revised regulations?

A. No, their duties are largely the same. Contractors must co-operate with each other and with the principal contractor to co-ordinate their work activities. Contractors should be competent for the work they are doing; plan, manage and monitor their own work to ensure health and safety; and provide suitable training for their workers to ensure their health and safety.

Q60. What if the job is not notifiable, and there is no principal contractor?

A. The contractor will be required to:

    i. Inform the client of the client's CDM duties if this has not already been done.

    ii. Plan, manage and monitor the construction work to ensure that it is carried out without risks to health and safety.

    iii. Provide information, training, and a suitable site induction for their workforce.

    iv. Ensure the site is suitably fenced and prevent access by unauthorised persons.

    v. Ensure that there are adequate welfare facilities for those working on the site.

Q61. Reg 13(6) requires contractors to prevent unauthorised access to sites, and Reg 27(2) requires sites to be identified with signs and/or fenced off. Isn't this the same thing?

A. No. Reg 13(6) requires the contractor to take reasonable steps to prevent unauthorised access to the site. This could be access by members of the public, site workers, visitors, or delivery drivers. For instance, the contractor may wish to control access to the site, and limit it to those who have received a site induction. Access may be controlled by a gate, a security guard, or turnstile system. A banksman may be used to control vehicles arriving at site.

Reg 27(2) deals with circumstances where there are risks to health and safety on the site, and it is necessary to use signage around the perimeter, or fence it off completely if the risks warrant this. For instance, painting work in an occupied office block may just be taped off with a warning sign. Pavement works in the street might have temporary barriers in place, but a larger construction site with greater hazards may require a hoarding or secure fencing.

PRE-CONSTRUCTION INFORMATION

Q62. As a client, do I still have to provide information about the site to contractors who I am thinking of appointing to carry out the work?

A. You need to provide those bidding for the work (or those who are preparing to carry out the work) with relevant information, in your possession or with information that can be obtained by sensible enquiries, including surveys and other investigations where necessary. This allows those bidding or preparing for the work to consider these hazards when making their bids or plans, and allows them to allocate resources to control the risks that will arise from these hazards. The level of detail of the information should be proportionate to the risks involved in the project.

Q63. As a client, do I have to provide information about asbestos that may be present in the structure?

A. Yes. You must provide this information so that those planning or bidding for the work can allocate resources for the control of asbestos. You should already hold information about the presence or otherwise of asbestos, but if you have no information, then you should arrange for a Type 3 survey to be carried out by a competent person. This is particularly important where the project involves demolition. It is not acceptable, for example, to inform others that '...there may be asbestos present on the site'. You must carry out a survey that identifies whether asbestos is present, and if so, where it is situated and what type it is.

Q64. What should a client provide as pre-construction information?

A. Guidance on what information you should provide can be found at Appendix 2 of the ACOP.

THE PLAN AND FILE

Q65. What is the difference between a Construction Phase Plan and a Health and Safety File?

A. The Principal Contractor prepares the Construction Phase Plan, to outline the arrangements for managing health and safety on site during construction work. Appendix 3 of the CDM 2007 ACOP provides detail on the topics to include in the Construction Phase Plan.

The Health and Safety File is prepared or revised by the CDM co-ordinator for notifiable projects. It will require the CDM Co-ordinator to liaise with several people, including client, designers, principal contractor and contractors. The File will contain information necessary for future construction, maintenance, refurbishment or demolition to be carried out safely, and is retained by the client or any future owner of the property. (Where a client gets non-notifiable work done, and a Health and Safety File already exists for the premises, it would be advisable for the client to update the file if necessary).

COMPETENCE

Q66. I have heard that competence is now a key issue in CDM 2007. Why is this?

A.   CDM competence is about being able to perform your health and safety requirements and avoiding contravening health and safety law. There is justifiable emphasis on competence, because it is generally recognised that competent people are safer. The duties in CDM 2007 work both ways. Persons making appointments have to take reasonable steps to ensure that those who are appointed are competent for what they are expected to do. Likewise, those accepting such appointments should only do so if they are competent to undertake the activity.

The new CDM 2007 ACOP now provides practical guidance to assist people in assessing competence. The advice given in the ACOP will make the assessment of corporate and individual competence easier.

Q67. How can I assure the competence of my site-based workforce?

A.   For basic construction trades, such as bricklayers, carpenters and painters and decorators, the achievement of an NVQ (or SVQ in Scotland) Level 2 qualification or higher will assure a level of competence in line with the requirements of CDM 2007.

The Construction Skills CSCS Health and Safety Test, a computer based multiple choice test which tests a basic level of health and safety knowledge, provides a good way of ensuring that new entrants have a threshold knowledge of health and safety. In other sectors, schemes such as the two-day CCNSG course in the Engineering Construction Sector provide an equivalent mechanism.

Possession of a CSCS card does mean that the individual has achieved a recognised level of competence, but employers need to be careful that the trade or work occupation on the card matches the work activity to be carried out, and that the actual level of experience and training of the individual is sufficient.

Where less experienced staff are engaged to carry out construction work, additional supervision must be provided to ensure that adequate risk control is achieved.

TRAINING MATERIAL & ADDITIONAL INFORMATION

Q68. Will HSE be producing any training material to assist my company in training key personnel for CDM 2007?

A. Yes. There will be a PowerPoint presentation available on the HSE website which anyone can access and use as they see fit. It may be necessary to edit it to suit the needs of the audience receiving it.

Further information can be obtained from:

i. Managing health and safety in construction, Construction (Design and Management) Regulations 2007, Approved Code of Practice, Available from HSE books (www.hsebooks.co.uk or 01787 881165).

ii. HSE Web site Construction pages (www.hse.gsi.gov.uk/construction)

iii. HSE Infoline 0845 345 0055

iv. The CDM Industry guidance for dutyholders (www.cskills.org/cdm)

ENFORCEMENT OF CDM 2007

Q69. Will CDM 2007 still just be enforced by HSE inspectors?

A. No. HSE inspectors for construction sites and premises normally enforced by HSE will enforce CDM 2007. In accordance with the Health and Safety (Enforcing Authority) Regulations 1998, local authorities will be able to enforce CDM for those premises where they are the enforcing authority, for minor internal, non segregated construction work. The local authorities will also have the option of dealing with relevant client and design issues for premises that they enforce for health and safety. The Office of the Rail Regulator will enforce CDM 2007 for construction work on operational railways.

ANNEX K - DIFFERENCES BETWEEN CDM 1994 AND CDM 2007

Summary of Key Changes in CDM 2007

i.   CDM and CHSW combined.

ii.   Regulations re-ordered to group duties together by dutyholder; and to show whether individual provisions apply to all projects, only notifiable projects or only nonnotifiable projects. ("Notifiable" is defined as before, but the application provision relating to fewer than 5 workers on site has been removed).

iii.   Domestic projects no longer need to be notified.

iv.   Demolition is treated in the same way as other construction activity except a written plan is required.

v.   Clients enhanced duties to ensure that the arrangements other dutyholders have made are sufficient to ensure the health and safety of those working on the project.

vi.   Client's agents and developers provisions removed; a group of clients involved in a project can now elect one to be the only CDM client.

vii.   Designers have a new duty to eliminate hazards and reduce remaining risks so far as is reasonably practicable. Also have duty to ensure that any workplace they design complies with relevant sections of the Workplace (Health, Safety and Welfare) Regulations 1992.

viii.   Planning supervisor ceases to exist. "CDM Co-ordinator" introduced to support and advise the client in discharging his duties and co-ordinate design and planning.

ix.   Appointment of a CDM co-ordinator or principal contractor, and a written health and safety plan only required for notifiable projects (but demolition work requires written system of work).

x.   Dutyholders cannot arrange for, or instruct anyone, to carry out or manage design or construction work unless that person is competent (or being supervised by someone who is); and cannot accept a CDM appointment/ engagement unless they are competent to carry it out.

xi.   Assessment and demonstration of competence simplified, with new core criteria and specific ACoP material on individual and corporate competence.

xii.   General co-operation and co-ordination duties on everyone involved in a project (relating to others on the same or adjoining sites); and a specific requirement to implement any preventive and protective measures on the basis of the principles specified in the Management Regulations.

xiii.   Clients now have the duty, (which already exists in the Health & Safety at Work Act and Management Regulations) to take reasonable steps to ensure that dutyholders' management arrangements (including time and other resources) are suitable to enable the construction work to be carried out, (and any related structure designed for use as a place of work can be used), without risk to health or safety. Clients have the duty to ensure that the arrangements are maintained and reviewed throughout the project.

xiv. Clients must tell designers and contractors how much time they have, before the start of work on site, for planning and preparing construction work.

xv. For notifiable projects, designers are prohibited from doing anything more than initial design work before the CDM coordinator has been appointed. In preparing or modifying a design they are required, so far as is reasonably practicable, to avoid risks to the health or safety of any person using a structure designed as a workplace. They must eliminate hazards that may give rise to risks and reduce risks from any remaining hazards.

xvi. The civil liability exemption has been removed in relation to employer/employee relationship. The Management Regulations have already been amended along these lines.

xvii. Various definitions have been changed, including those of "client", "construction phase plan", "construction work", "contractor", "design" and "designer", "place of work" and "structure".

ANNEX L - DIFFERENCES BETWEEN CHSW 1996 AND CDM 2007

1996 Reg No.	Construction (Health Safety & Welfare Regulations) 1996	2007 Reg No.	Part 4 Construction (Health Safety & Welfare Regulations) 2007
4. Persons upon whom duties are imposed	(1) It shall be the duty of every employer… (2) It shall be the duty of every person who controls the way in which… (3) It shall be the duty of every employee carrying out construction work to comply with the requirements.	25. Application	(1) Every Contractor carrying out construction work shall comply… (2) Every person (other than a contractor carrying out construction work) who controls the way in which any construction work is carried out….
5. Safe places of work	(2) Every place of work shall, so far as is reasonably practicable, be made and kept safe for, **and without risks to health to**, any person at work there. (3) Suitable and sufficient steps shall be taken to ensure, so far as is reasonably practicable, that no person gains access to any place which does not comply with the requirements of paragraphs (1) or (2) (4) Paragraphs (1) to (3) shall not apply in relation to a person engaged in work for the purpose of making any place safe, provided all practicable steps are taken to ensure the safety of that person whilst engaged in that work. (5) Every place of work shall, so far as is reasonably practicable and having regard to the nature of the work being carried out there, have sufficient working space and be so arranged that it is suitable for any person who is working or who is likely to work there.	26. Safe places of work	(2) Every place of work shall, so far as is reasonably practicable, be made and kept safe for any person at work there. (3) Suitable and sufficient steps shall be taken to ensure, so far as is reasonably practicable, that no person **uses access or egress**, or gains access to any place which does not comply with the requirements of paragraphs (1) or (2) **Whole text omitted** (4) Now includes the text... Every place of work shall, so far as is reasonably practicable and having regard to the nature of the work being carried out there, have sufficient working space and be so arranged that it is suitable for any person who is working or who is likely to work there **taking into account of any necessary work equipment present**.
26. Good order	(2) Where necessary in the interests of health and safety, the perimeter of a construction site shall, so far as is reasonably practicable, be identified by suitable signs and the site shall be so arranged that its extent is readily identifiable.	27. Good order & site security	(2) Where necessary in the interests of health and safety, the perimeter of a construction site shall, so far as is reasonably practicable **and in accordance with the level of risk posed either** –

			(a) have its perimeter identified by suitable signs & so be arranged that its extent is readily identifiable: or (b) **be fenced off, or both**
	(3) No timber or other material with projecting nails shall— (a) be used in any work in which the nails may be a source of danger to any person; or (b) be allowed to remain in any place where the nails may be a source of danger to any person.		(3) No timber or other material with projecting nails (**or other similar object**) shall – (a) be used in any work: or (b) be allowed to remain in any place, if the nails may be a source of danger to any person
9. Stability of structures	(1) All practicable steps shall be taken, where necessary to prevent danger to any person, to ensure that any new or existing structure or any part of such structure which may become unstable or in a temporary state of weakness or instability due to the carrying out of construction work (**including any excavation work**) does not collapse **accidentally**.	28. Stability of structures	(1) All practicable steps shall be taken, where necessary to prevent danger to any person, to ensure that any new or existing structure or any part of such structure that may become unstable or in a temporary state of weakness or instability due to the carrying out of construction work does not collapse.
	(3) Any buttress, temporary support or temporary structure used to support a permanent structure pursuant to paragraph (1) **shall be erected or dismantled only under the supervision of a competent person**.		(2) Any buttress, temporary support or temporary structure **must be of such design & so installed & maintained as to withstand any foreseeable loads which maybe imposed on it, & must only be used for the purpose for which it is designed, installed & maintained**.
10. Demolition or dismantling	(1) Suitable and sufficient steps shall be taken to ensure that the demolition or dismantling of any structure, or any part of any structure, being demolition or dismantling which gives rise to a risk of danger to any person, is planned and carried out in such a manner as to prevent, so far as is practicable, such danger.	29. Demolition or dismantling	(1) **The demolition or dismantling, or part of a structure, shall be carried out in such a manner as to prevent, or, where it is not practicable to prevent it, to reduce danger to as low a level as is reasonably practicable**. –
	(2) Demolition or dismantling to which paragraph (1) applies shall be planned and carried out only under the supervision of a competent person.		(2) **The arrangements for carrying out such demolition or dismantling shall be recorded in writing before the demolition or dismantling work begins**
11. Explosives		30. Explosives	(1) **So far as is reasonably practicable, explosives shall be stored, transported & used safely & security**.

12. Excavations	(1) All practicable steps shall be taken, where necessary to prevent danger to any person, to ensure that any new or existing excavation or any part of such excavation that may be in a temporary state of weakness **or instability due to the carrying out of construction work** (**including other excavation work**) does not collapse accidentally. (2) Suitable and sufficient steps shall be taken to prevent, so far as is reasonably practicable, any person from being buried or trapped by a fall or dislodgement of any material.	31. Excavations	(1) All practicable steps shall be taken, where necessary to prevent danger to any person, including where necessary the provision of supports or battering to ensure that- (a) any excavation or part of an excavation does not collapse accidentally. (b) no material from a side or roof or, or adjacent to, any excavation is dislodged or falls, and (c) no person is buried or trapped in an excavation by material which is dislodged or falls
	(4) Suitable and sufficient equipment for supporting an excavation shall be provided to ensure that the requirements of paragraphs (1) to (3) may be complied with.		**Whole text omitted**
	(5) The installation, alteration or dismantling of any support for an excavation pursuant to paragraphs (1), (2) or (3) shall be carried out only under the supervision of a competent person.		**Whole text omitted**
	(7) Where a collapse of an excavation would endanger any person, no material, vehicle or plant and equipment shall be placed or moved near any excavation where it is likely to **cause such collapse**.		(3) suitable & sufficient steps shall be taken where necessary, to prevent any part of an excavation or ground adjacent to it from being **overloaded** by work equipment or material
	Schedule 7 equivalent		(4) Construction work shall not be carried out in an excavation where any supports or battering have been provided, unless- (a) the excavation & any work equipment & materials which affect its safety, have been inspected by a competent person – (i) at the start of every shift in which the work is to be carried out, (ii) after the event likely to have affected the strength or stability of the excavation, & (iii) after the unintentional falls or dislodgement, & (b) the person who carried out the inspection is stratified that the work can be carried out there safely.

	Reg 29 equivalent		(5) **where a person who carried out the inspection has under Reg 33 (1) (a) informed the person on whose behalf the inspection was carried out of any matter he is not satisfied, work shall not be carried out in the excavation until the matters have been satisfactory remedied.**
13. Cofferdams and caissons	(1) Every cofferdam or caisson and **every part thereof shall** be of suitable design and construction, **of suitable and sound material and of sufficient strength and capacity** for the purpose for which it is used, and shall be properly maintained.	32. Cofferdams and caissons	(1) Every cofferdam or caisson shall be – (a) of suitable design and construction, (b) **appropriately equipped so that workers can gain shelter or escape if water or materials enter it**, & (c) properly maintained
	Schedule 7 equivalent		(2) A cofferdam or caisson shall be used to carry out construction work only if -- (a) the cofferdam or caisson & any work equipment & materials which affect its safety, have been inspected by a competent person- (i) at the start of every shift in which the work is to be carried out (ii) after the event likely to have affected the strength or stability of the cofferdam or caisson, & (b) the person who carried out the inspection is stratified that the work can be carried out there safely.
	Reg 29 equivalent		(3) **where a person who carried out the inspection has under Reg 33 (1) (a) informed the person on whose behalf the inspection was carried out of any matter he is not stratified, work shall not be carried out in the cofferdam or caisson until the matters have been satisfactory remedied.**
	(2) **The construction, installation, alteration or dismantling of a cofferdam or caisson shall take place only under the supervision of a competent person**.		Superseded by CDM competence requirements
30. Reports		33. Reports	(1) Subject to paragraph 5, the persons carrying out the inspection under Reg 31& 32 shall, before the end of the shift within the which the inspection is completed – (b) prepare a report which shall include the particulars set out in schedule 3.

			(3) **where the person owing a duty is an employee or works under the control of another, his employer or, as the case may be, the person under whose control he works shall ensure that he performs his duty.**
12. Excavations	(8) No excavation work shall be carried out unless suitable and sufficient steps have been taken to identify and, so far as is reasonably practicable, prevent any risk of injury arising from any underground cable or other underground service.	34. Energy distribution installations	(5) **no construction work which is liable to create a risk to health & safety from an underground service, or from damage to or disturbance of it, shall be carried out unless suitable & sufficient (including any steps required by this regulation) have been taken to prevent such risk, so far as is reasonably practicable**
		34. Energy distribution installations	(1) **where necessary to prevent danger, energy distribution installations shall be suitably located, checked & clearly indicated.** (2) **where there is a risk from electric power cables-** **(a) they shall be directed away from the area of risk, or –** **(b) the power shall be cut of, or** **(c) if it is not reasonably practicable to comply with (a) or (b), suitable warning notices & -** **(i) barriers suitable for excluding work equipment which is not needed,** **(ii) or where vehicles need to pass beneath the cables, suspended protections, or** **(iii) in either case, measures providing an equivalent level of safety, shall be provided or (in the case of measures) taken.**
14. Prevention of drowning	(3) Any vessel used to convey any person by water to or from a place of work— **(a) shall be of suitable construction; and** **(b) shall be properly maintained; and** (c) shall be under the control of a competent person; and (d) shall not be overcrowded or overloaded.	35. Prevention of drowning	(3) Any vessel used to convey any person by water to or from a place of work shall not be overcrowded or overloaded. **Additional provisions now covered by PUWER**
15. Traffic routes	(1) Every construction site shall be organised in such a way that, so far as is reasonably practicable, pedestrians and vehicles can move	36. Traffic routes	(1) Every construction site shall be organised in such a way, that so far as is reasonably practicable, pedestrians and vehicles can move

	safely **and without risk to health** (3) Without prejudice to the generality of paragraph (2), traffic routes shall not satisfy the requirements of that paragraph unless suitable and sufficient steps are taken to ensure that - (b) any door or gate used or intended to be used by pedestrians and which leads onto a traffic route for vehicles is sufficiently separated from that traffic route to enable pedestrians from a place of safety to see any approaching vehicle or plant;		safely (3) a traffic routes shall not satisfy sub paragraph 2 unless suitable & sufficient steps are taken to ensure that – **(b) any door or gate for pedestrians which lead onto a traffic route is sufficiently separated from it to enable them from a place of safety to see any approaching vehicle**, - (4) every traffic route shall be – (a) indicated by suitable signs where necessary for the reasons of health & safety, **(b) regularly checked , &** **(c) properly maintained**.
	(4) No vehicle shall be driven on a traffic route unless, so far as is reasonably practicable, that traffic route is free from obstruction and permits sufficient clearance.		(5) No vehicle shall be driven on a traffic route unless, so far as is reasonably practicable, that traffic route is free from obstruction and permits sufficient clearance
	(5) **Where it is not reasonably practicable to comply with all or any of the requirements of paragraph (4), suitable and sufficient steps shall be taken to warn the driver of the vehicle and any other person riding thereon of any approaching obstruction or lack of clearance**.		Text omitted
16 Doors and Gates	(1) Where necessary to prevent the risk of injury to any person, any door, gate or hatch (including a temporary door, gate or hatch) shall incorporate or be fitted with suitable safety devices.		**Text omitted** **Now covered in Workplace regs**.
	(2) Without prejudice to the generality of paragraph (1), a door, gate or hatch shall not comply with that paragraph unless-- (a) Any sliding door, gate or hatch has a device to prevent it coming off its track during use; (b) Any upward opening door, gate or hatch has a device to prevent it falling back; (c) Any powered door, gate or hatch has suitable and effective features to prevent it causing injury by		

	trapping any person; (d) Where necessary for reasons of health or safety, any powered door, gate or hatch can be operated manually unless it opens automatically if the power fails. (3) This regulation shall not apply to any door, gate or hatch forming part of any mobile plant and equipment.		
17. Vehicles	(4) No person shall ride or be required or permitted to ride on any vehicle being used for the purposes of construction work otherwise than in a safe place thereon provided for that purpose. (6) **Where any vehicle is used for excavating or handling (including tipping) materials**, suitable and sufficient measures shall be taken so as to prevent such vehicle from falling into any excavation or pit, or into water, or overrunning the edge of any embankment or earthwork (7) **Suitable plant and equipment shall be provided and used for replacing on its track or otherwise safely moving any rail vehicle which may become derailed**.	37. Vehicles	(4) No person shall ride or be required or permitted to ride on any vehicle being used for the purposes of construction work otherwise than in a safe place thereon provided for that purpose. (6), suitable and sufficient measures shall be taken so as to prevent such vehicle from falling into any excavation or pit, or into water, or overrunning the edge of any embankment or earthwork **Text**
19. Emergency routes and exits	(1) Where necessary in the interests of the health and safety of any person on a construction site, a sufficient number of suitable emergency routes and exits shall be provided to enable any person to reach a place of safety quickly in the event of danger. (2) An emergency route or exit provided pursuant to paragraph (1) shall lead as directly as possible to an identified safe area (3) Any emergency route and exit provided in accordance with paragraph (1), and any traffic route **or door** giving access thereto, shall be kept clear and free from obstruction, and, where necessary, provided with emergency lighting so that such emergency route or exit may be used at any time. (4) Any provision for emergency routes and exits made under paragraph (1) shall have regard to –	40. Emergency routes and exits	(1) Where necessary in the interests of the health and safety of any person on a construction site a sufficient number of suitable emergency routes and exits shall be provided to enable any person to reach a place of safety quickly in the event of danger. (2) 2 An emergency route or exit provided pursuant to paragraph (1) shall lead as directly as possible to an identified safe area (3) Any emergency route and exit provided in accordance with paragraph (1), and any traffic route giving access thereto, shall be kept clear and free from obstruction, and, where necessary, provided with emergency lighting so that such emergency route or exit may be used at any time (3) **In making arrangements under paragraph (1), account shall be taken of the matters in regulation 39(2)**

	(a) the type of work for which the construction site is being used; (b) the characteristics and size of the construction site and the number and location of places of work on that site; (c) the plant and equipment being used; (d) the number of persons likely to be present on the site at any one time; and (e) the physical and chemical properties of any substances or materials on or likely to be on the site.		
	(5) All emergency routes or exits shall be indicated by suitable signs.		(5) All emergency routes or exits shall be indicated by suitable signs.
20. Emergency procedures	(1) Where necessary in the interests of the health and safety of any person on a construction site, there shall be prepared and, when necessary, implemented suitable and sufficient arrangements for dealing with any foreseeable emergency, which arrangements shall include procedures for any necessary evacuation of the site or any part thereof.	39. Emergency procedures	(1) Where necessary in the interests of the health and safety of any person on a construction site, there shall be prepared and, when necessary, implemented suitable and sufficient arrangements for dealing with any foreseeable emergency, which arrangements shall include procedures for any necessary evacuation of the site or any part thereof..
	(2) Without prejudice to the generality of paragraph (1), arrangements prepared pursuant to that paragraph shall – (a) have regard to those matters set out in paragraph (4) of regulation 19; (b) **designate an adequate number of persons who will implement the arrangements; and** (c) **include any necessary contacts with the external emergency services, particularly as regards rescue work and fire fighting**		(2)In making arrangements under paragraph (1), account shall be taken of - (a) the type of work for which the construction site is being used; (b) the characteristics and size of the construction site and the number and location of places of work on that site; (c) the plant and equipment being used; (d) the number of persons likely to be present on the site at any one time; and (d) the physical and chemical properties of any substances or materials on or likely to be on the site.
	(3) Where arrangements are prepared pursuant to paragraph (1), suitable and sufficient steps shall be taken to ensure that— (a) every person to whom the arrangements extend is familiar with those arrangements; and		(3) Where arrangements are prepared pursuant to paragraph (1), suitable and sufficient steps shall be taken to ensure that— (a) every person to whom the arrangements extend is familiar with those arrangements; and

	(b) the arrangements are tested by being put into effect at suitable intervals.		(b) the arrangements are tested by being put into effect at suitable intervals
21. Fire detection and firefighting	(1) **Without prejudice to the provisions of any other enactment**, there shall be provided on a construction site where necessary in the interests of the health and safety of any person at work on that site— (a) suitable and sufficient fire-fighting equipment; and (b) suitable and sufficient fire detectors and alarm systems, which shall be suitably located.	21. Fire detection and firefighting	(1) where necessary in the interest of health & safety of any person at work on a construction site there shall be provided suitable and sufficient (a) fire-fighting equipment; and (b) suitable and sufficient fire detectors and alarm systems, which shall be suitably located.
	(6) Where a work activity may give rise to a particular risk of fire, a person shall not carry out such work unless he is suitably instructed so as to prevent, **so far as is reasonably practicable, that risk**.		(6) Where a work activity may give rise to a particular risk of fire, a person shall not carry out such work unless he is suitably instructed
24. Temperature and weather protection	(1) Suitable and sufficient steps shall be taken to ensure, so far as is reasonably practicable, that during working hours the temperature at **any indoor place of work to which these Regulations apply** is reasonable having regard to the purpose for which that place is used.	43. Temperature and weather protection	(1) Suitable and sufficient steps shall be taken to ensure, so far as is reasonably practicable, that during working hours the temperature at **any place of work indoors** is reasonable having regard to the purpose for which that place is used
	(2)Every place of work outdoors shall, where necessary to ensure the health and safety of persons at work there, be so arranged that, so far as is reasonably practicable and having regard to the purpose for which that place is used and any protective clothing **or equipment** provided for the use of any person at work there, it provides protection from adverse weather.		2) Every place of work outdoors shall, where necessary to ensure the health and safety of persons at work there, be so arranged that, so far as is reasonably practicable and having regard to the purpose for which that place is used and any protective clothing **or work equipment** provided for the use of any person at work there, it provides protection from adverse weather.
28. Training	Any person who carries out any activity involving construction work where training, technical knowledge or experience is necessary to reduce the risks of injury to any person shall possess such training, knowledge or experience, or be under such degree of supervision by a person having such training, knowledge or experience, as may be appropriate having regard to the nature of the activity.		**Text omitted** **Replaced by Reg 13 training requirement in CDM**

| 21. Welfare facilities | Facilities for rest Schedule 6. Rest facilities shall—
(a) include rest facilities provided in one or more rest rooms or rest areas;
(b) include rest rooms or rest areas with suitable arrangements to protect non-smokers from discomfort caused by tobacco smoke;
(c) where necessary, include suitable facilities for any person at work who is a pregnant woman or nursing mother to rest;
(d) include suitable arrangements to ensure that meals can be prepared and eaten; and
(e) include the means for boiling water. | Schedule 2 | Facilities for rest
14 (1) Suitable & sufficient rest rooms or rest areas shall be provided or made available at readily accessible places

(2) rest rooms & rest areas shall –
(a) include suitable arrangements to protect non-smokers from discomfort caused by tobacco smoke;
(b) be equipped with an adequate number of tables & adequate seating with backs for the number of persons at work likely to use them at any one time,
(c) where necessary, include suitable facilities for any person at work who is a pregnant woman or nursing mother to rest **lying down**;
(d) include suitable arrangements to ensure that meals can be prepared and eaten; and
(e) include the means for boiling water
(f) be maintained at an appropriate temperature |

ANNEX M - CDM 2007 – CHSW REQUIREMENTS

Previously all the management software requirements for the planning and control of construction projects were contained in the CDM Regulations. Hardware requirements (trench support, welfare facilities, traffic routes, vehicles etc) were addressed in the completely separate Construction (Health Safety and Welfare) Regulations. The new regulations combine both the hardware and software requirements into a single set of new regulations called CDM.

Parts 2 and 3 deal with all the management software requirements

Part 4 deals with the hardware requirements.

It is important to understand that parts 2 & 3 are separate from Part 4. The relationship can be understood as Part 4 defining **minimum** physical standards that must be in place during construction work, whereas Parts 2 & 3 describe a management framework for achieving them.

Who is responsible for what in providing the hardware?

Part 4 creates different duties for different people depending on what their roles are in providing physical requirements, on site, during construction work, as it happens. Understanding these different duties is important if confusion (and possibly conflict) between different parties over who is meant to be doing what is to be avoided.

Because parts 2 & 3 are separate from Part 4, Part 4 sets out its own duties for compliance with the hardware standards it describes. The key elements are Regulations 25(1) and 25(2) which has a general approach which states that the primary responsibility rests with those who are actually doing the work. Others must also be held responsible but only if they are genuinely exercising control over what is going on.

25(1) can only apply to those who are actually doing construction work. Merely being involved with construction work in some way or another is not enough to trigger the duty in Regulation 25(1). For instance clients will frequently be involved in construction work, but unless they are actually doing the construction work themselves they do not hold a duty under 25(1). The contractor actually doing the work clearly does.

Regulation 25(2) is designed to place a duty on those who whilst not actually doing the work themselves, effectively 'call the shots' for those who are. It is clearly the case that such people should not escape responsibility to exercise that control responsibly.

The key phrase is '**controls the way in which any construction work is carried out**': So for the duty to be triggered real control over the working method and circumstances has to be exercised.

For instance a client may say to a contractor who is going to do the work 'start on Tuesday'. This would not be enough to trigger the duty in 25(2). Defining a start date does not amount to controlling the method or circumstances. Alternatively the client may say 'you can start on Tuesday and I am not going to divert the adjacent traffic route.' Failure to divert the traffic route could lead to non-compliance with the requirements in Regulation 36 if the work goes ahead. Since this situation has arisen because of the positive decision of the client, the client could be held accountable under Regulation 25(2) as well as the contractor under 25(1).

In both Regulations 25(1) and 25(2) the extent of control is important in deciding the extent of the legal duty held. The key phrase is 'matters within his control'

In practice contractors carrying out construction work themselves will normally have a clear cut duty not to let their people carry on working, unless all the necessary safeguards are in place It is possibly a little more complex in Regulation 25(2), where it uses the word control twice in the same regulation:

i. 'controls the way in which any construction work is carried out'; and

ii. 'comply with the requirements of regulations 26-44 insofar as they relate to matters which are within his control'

These need to be read in order. If eg a client or a principal contractor decides for anyone else to any extent how construction work is actually going to be done then this confirms that Regulation 25(2) applies to them. The second reference ie 'matters within his control' can then be used to determine the extent of the Regulation 25(2) duty.

For instance Regulation 34 requires that, if it is reasonably practicable to do so, electric cables are either rerouted or isolated before work takes place adjacent to them. If it is not reasonably practicable to do this then alternative measures to exclude unnecessary access, or provide warning of overhead cables to vehicles or something equivalent are required.

A client or principal contractor may decide that cables are not going to be either re-routed or isolated. Instead contractors doing the work are required to rely on providing overhead warnings instead. In this case the traffic route concerned was a busy one and it would have been straightforward putting the overhead cable underground during site preparatory work. The contractor whose vehicles were using the route accepted the responsibility to provide overhead warning protection, but as time passed it fell down and he failed to repair it.

The starting point is that the client or principal contractor has undoubtedly exercised some control over the work method by dictating that it took place without disconnecting or re-routing the power line. Thus he has a duty under Regulation 25(2). The next question is how far that duty extended and that depends on the extent of the control he exercised. He dictated that the power line remained and was clearly exercising control over that issue. Thus he can be held accountable for the failure to move or disconnect the power line when it was reasonably practicable to do so. The other issue is the failure to ensure the overhead protection was in place. The contractor was the one with the responsibility and resources to do this. Client or principal contractor had little if any direct control over making sure this happened, certainly on a day to day basis. Consequently it is much less likely that either could be held accountable as far as the failure in providing the overhead protection is concerned. The contractor has the lead accountability.

Regulation 25 is not the same as regulation 9

This potential Regulation 25 duty on clients should not be confused with the Regulation 9 requirement on clients to ensure arrangements are made for managing the project. The regulation 25 duty deals explicitly with the provision of physical safeguards as the work is happening. Regulation 9 is all about the client's contribution to creating the wider management environment to facilitate delivery of the physical safeguards. There may be shortcomings in a client's response to Regulation 9. This does not necessarily mean that any subsequent physical shortcomings on site trigger a client breach of Regulation 25.

For instance a client may have taken no meaningful interest in the principal contractor's effective delivery of the construction phase plan. At the same time the principal contractor may have been doing nothing meaningful to ensure that what he says should happen in the plan really does. As a result poor site standards prevail and, for instance, excavations have become insecurely supported. In this case

i. The principal contractor could be called to account for failing to implement his plan Regulation 23(1);

ii. The contractor whose employees work in the excavation could be called to account for failing to comply with Part 4 standards on excavation support (Regulation 25(1));

iii. And the client could be called to account for failing to take reasonable steps to ensure that project management arrangements were such that other duty holders did what they should (Regulation 9 (1)(a)

But it is unlikely that the client could be held directly accountable under regulation 25(2) for the failure to comply with Part 4 physical standards on excavation support. Because he exercised no explicit control over the way that that construction was carried out – which is a different matter from the management environment in which it took place.

What are the physical requirements in Part 4?

For the most part they are unchanged from those in the Construction (Health Safety and Welfare) Regulations. There are some detailed changes (described below) but in essence the policy aim was to merely reproduce existing hardware requirements in the new regulations.

There are no requirements relating to falls from height issues. Falls from height issues were removed from the CHSW regulations and replaced by the cross-sector Work at Height Regulations in 2005.

Demolition

Probably the most important change is in respect of demolition and/or dismantling of structures. Regulation 29(1) requires that this is both planned and carried out in such a manner to prevent danger, or if that is not reasonably practicable, to reduce it to as low a level as reasonably practicable.

Regulation 29(2) further requires that that the arrangements for demolition/dismantling shall be recorded in writing before the work begins

These requirements apply to all demolition or structural dismantling. Demolition and dismantling means the same thing in the new CDM as it did in the old. So while it includes the deliberate destruction or dismantling of a structure, making door openings or removing non structural components, on their own, are not included.

It makes no difference whether the work is notifiable or not, or whether it is contained within the scope of a wider CDM project. If it is demolition or it is structural dismantling, it **must** be planned and there **must** be a written plan before the work starts. This will usually be in the form of a method statement or similar document. As with all such documents they need to be sufficiently task specific to deal adequately with the risks involved.

The obvious goal is that in demolition and dismantling everyone knows precisely what they are going to do and why **before** they do it and when they do it, it is done the right way.

Site security

There is a specific requirement that, where necessary for health and safety reasons construction sites are

   i.   fenced off; or

   ii.   arranged so that the perimeter is identifiable and marked by signs

Energy distribution installations

Regulation 34(1) requires that energy distribution installations are suitably located, checked and clearly identified. This is a new requirement, but in practice it should add nothing new for those who are already complying with good practice standards on design and use of temporary energy supplies on construction sites.

Regulation 34(2) requires that wherever there is a risk from electric power cables they are moved or isolated if it is reasonably practicable to do so. If it is not then

i.   Either barriers to exclude unnecessary work equipment; or

ii. Suspended protection where vehicles need to pass under cables; or

iii. Other measure providing equivalent protection

Must be provided. Again, whilst these explicit requirements are new on the face of the law, they should add nothing new for those who are already complying with well known good practice standards.

Fire and emergency procedures

Most workplace fire safety requirements are now dealt with in the Regulatory Reform (Fire Safety) Order 2005. However fire safety on construction sites continues to be dealt with by specific regulations in Part 4 of the new CDM Regulations (Regulations 38 – 41). These regulations carry over what was contained in the 1996 CHSW Regulations. Note though that these only apply with respect to construction sites. Where construction sites interface with other work areas then fire safety compliance with CDM on the construction site will need to be integrated with Regulatory Reform Order compliance in the workplace next to it. This means co-operation between those managing the site and the adjacent workplace.

N. REFERENCES AND FURTHER READING

Management of health and safety at work. Management of Health and Safety at Work Regulations 1999. Approved Code of Practice and guidance L21 (Second edition)

Work with materials containing asbestos. Control of Asbestos Regulations 2006. Approved Code of Practice and guidance L143 HSE Books 2006

Workplace health, safety and welfare. Workplace (Health, Safety and Welfare) Regulations 1992. Approved Code of Practice L24 HSE Books 1992

The Building Regulations 2000 SI 2000/2531 The Stationery Office 2000 Safety representatives and safety committees L87 (Third edition) HSE Books

A guide to the Health and Safety (Consultation with Employees) Regulations 1996. Guidance on Regulations L95 HSE Books 1996 ISBN 0 7176 1234 1

An introduction to health and safety: Health and safety in small businesses Leaflet INDG259(rev1) HSE Books 2003 (single copy free) Web version: www.hse.gov.uk/pubns/indg259.pdf

A guide to the Reporting of Injuries, Diseases and Dangerous Occurrences Regulations 1995 L73 (Second edition) HSE Books 1999

The Construction Confederation – www.thecc.org.uk

The Health and Safety Executive – www.hse.gov.uk

The Institute of Occupational Safety and Health – http://www.iosh.co.uk/

The Specialist Engineering Contractors Group– http://www.secgroup.org.uk/

The Engineering Contractors Industry Association - http://www.ecia.co.uk/

The Association of Project Safety - http://www.associationforprojectsafety.co.uk/

ConstructionSkills - http://www.citb-constructionskills.co.uk/

The Construction Clients Group –

http://www.constructingexcellence.org.uk/sectorforums/constructionclientsgroup/

The Federation of Master Builders - www.fmb.org.uk/

The National Federation of Builders - http://www.builders.org.uk/nfb/

The Construction Industry Council - http://www.cic.org.uk/

Union of Construction, Allied Trades and Technicians - http://www.ucatt.org.uk/